cfn

Acknowledgements

I would like to thank John Addyman, Mike Brown, Tony Hall-Patch, Adrian Jarvis, Mike Johnson, Bob Longridge, Miles Macnair, Bob Roper, Mike Brown, Bob Longridge and Hugh Torrens for their helpful discussions, encouragement and several references. Also to those who gave permission to reproduce material.

Published by The Rocket Press, Newcastle upon Tyne.

ISBN: 0 9535 1621 0

Designed and produced by Differentia Design
www.differentia.co.uk

Printed in England.

Typeset in ITC Cheltenham BT and News Gothic BT.

Contents

PREFACE

This book is aimed at those with an interest in understanding the contribution made by Robert Stephenson to the development of steam locomotive design in the early years of railway expansion; but in the hope that it will also appeal to a general readership, a chronology of the main events of his life has been included as an Appendix.

The main text covers the period from his birth in 1803 to the autumn of 1833, by which time all the most significant improvements to his locomotives had been made, culminating in the *Patentee* of that year. The writer has drawn heavily from period publications, especially his only major biographer Jeaffreson, and contemporary documents. Since Robert's death in 1859 other books have been written about his life, but usually in combination with that of his father George. It seems extraordinary that so significant an engineer as Robert Stephenson should have remained as neglected as he has, despite the honours he received during his lifetime, culminating in his burial in Westminster Abbey, a privilege only once before accorded an engineer, Thomas Telford. That he was far more than an engineer has been highlighted recently by a series of studies edited by Michael Bailey and published in 2003 under the title *Robert Stephenson: Eminent Engineer* to coincide with the bicentenary of his birth.

One of The Robert Stephenson Trust's objectives is to bring Robert Stephenson's achievements to the notice of today's public, partly in the hope that his life story will inspire a new generation of engineers and innovators. This book has been written by the Trust's founder, Vicky Haworth, who has had the good fortune to live in the house in Newcastle upon Tyne to which Robert brought his bride Frances Sanderson in 1829. This knowledge sparked Vicky's interest in finding out more about his life, for which she was well qualified as a researcher of late mediaeval architects. She soon found out that even contemporaneous accounts of Stephenson's work were contradictory, partly because of the shadow cast by his father. She was able to show that the *Rocket*, winner of the Rainhill Trials for the Liverpool & Manchester Railway, was actually instigated and designed by Robert and not George. And later, in 1986 it was Vicky Haworth who first realised the danger of a historic building - 20 South Street, Newcastle upon Tyne, the last vestige of an extensive range of factory premises comprising the firm of 'Robert Stephenson & Co' - being demolished. Through her efforts, a Trust was formed, facts marshalled, and the premises accorded a Grade II* listing. It is now restored and the base for the Robert Stephenson Trust.

The Trustees are extremely grateful to Vicky for committing so much of her time to compiling *The Making of a Prodigy,* especially under very difficult personal circumstances. We have only been able to publish it because of a grant provided by the Heritage Lottery Fund and by drawing on a legacy from the late Bill Tuck, founder Trustee and Stephenson enthusiast. It is our hope that the Trust will be able to produce further books from time to time. Readers may like to know that a biography entitled *Robert Stephenson: Railway Engineer* written by John Addyman and Vicky Haworth will be published by the North Eastern Railway Association in 2005.

Finally, I am grateful to Mike Brown, RST Trustee and former Chairman, for his patience and persistance in bringing this project to a successful conclusion.

Bob Longridge, Trust Chairman

INTRODUCTION

Robert Stephenson was called *'the greatest engineer of the present century.'*[1] No one challenged this emphatic eulogy made after his death on 12 October 1859. Robert's colleagues ensured a resting place in the nave of Westminster Abbey. Joseph Locke, President of the Institution of Civil Engineers, was a pallbearer. Members of his profession; age-long associates in other fields of interests, notably the Electric Telegraph Company of which he was President, surrounded the grave placed centrally in the Nation's mausoleum. Few were present out of duty. Communication being the key word of his ambition, everyone throughout the civilised world travelling for anything other than a short distance went by train, powered by what had become universally known as the Stephenson locomotive.

At the vast railway stations of large towns, the brightly painted locomotives converged, steaming, puffing and gently simmering. These magnificent dragons had replaced the work-horse within a generation. From the onset Robert Stephenson had insisted on using iron roofs to protect the trains and passengers from the elements, the first being at Curzon Street Birmingham and then Euston, London, the termini stations of the London & Birmingham Railway 1833-38. He employed the best architects to design the station buildings in both large and small towns to serve the railways. With comfortable waiting rooms heated by large fires, restaurants and bars, they became meeting places as well as waiting rooms, a new type of public house. Travelling by train had become fast, safe and comfortable: an extremely civilising experience for everyone. Robert Stephenson epitomised progress.

Beyond the persona publicly acknowledged, Robert Stephenson was a sensitive, private and often lonely man. His recollections were of an only son of an only parent. For the formative years of his life, he lived an almost claustrophobic existence with a much revered father. The fireplace in their only living room was the focus of their lives, a means of escape from each other's presence until he was thirteen being a loft room reached by a ladder. Animated discussions took place by the fireside concerning the utilisation of steam power. To translate the dream into reality was extremely difficult, mostly due to conservative notions and manufacturing limitations. It took a great deal of concentrated effort and dedication in order to overcome these problems.

TYNESIDE: *the first nineteen years*

To the Stephenson household came Richard Trevithick, first at Willington Quay near Newcastle upon Tyne, where Robert Stephenson was born 16 October 1803, and then at Paradise Row, West Moor, Killingworth. Having invented the high pressure steam engine, Trevithick visited North East collieries in order to promote and hopefully sell his patent engine by means of a working demonstration model mounted on wheels. Realising that without the necessity of a condenser his light compact machine could be used either as a tractive or stationary power, he designed various versions to be dual purpose. A model moving backwards and forwards must have been one of the most memorable subconscious recollections for a small child.

Robert's extrovert father George enjoyed entertaining and welcomed the excitement of new ideas. George Stephenson was also ambitious and within a short time climbed up the job ladder from assistant steam engine fireman to brakesman by the time of his marriage to Frances Henderson in November 1802. He aspired to be an enginewright and emulate his superior Robert Hawthorn, *'the cleverest enginewright of the district'.*[2]

Robert's birthplace

Trevithick's Model Locomotive c. 1802

When Frances became pregnant for the second time, a decision was made to leave Willington Quay for the rural parish of Longbenton. Their new cottage with one ground floor room and a loft, formed the western end of Paradise Row, a terrace built for the work force associated with the recent sinking of a pit at West Moor near to the old settlement of Killingworth. Retaining a post as brakesman, for once George Stephenson moved against his monetary instincts and almost certainly for the good of his wife's health.

Members of George Stephenson's mechanics meeting group to *'exchange views on difficult jobs'*[3] now included John Steele, Trevithick's chief mechanic chosen to construct a travelling engine, first in 1803 at the Pen-y-darran Iron Works in South Wales when the product of his success ran on a plateway in February 1804 and then at Whinfield's manufactory in Pipewellgate, Gateshead. Commissioned by the Wylam colliery owner Christopher Blackett, this custom-designed locomotive had a horizontal cylinder, flanged wheels to run on smooth rails and a wrought iron boiler. Weighing only 4½ tons, the intention was to minimize the engine's impact on the wooden rails of Blackett's waggonway which ran a distance of five miles from Wylam to the staiths at Lemington. Ironically, being light the locomotive was not adopted for its purpose due to the widely held misconception of a lack of adhesion. Although Trevithick had proved that smooth wheels would run on a smooth rail, his immediate successors still had doubts.

Many interested people packed Whinfield's yard to *'see her run'*[4] in May 1805. Young Robert would be taken to the demonstration trial at Gateshead. His pregnant mother was terminally ill from tuberculosis and would welcome periods of quiet rest. A large machine raising steam and moving would leave a lasting impression on a young mind. John Steele continually prophesied: *'the day would come when the locomotive engine would be fairly tried and would then be found to answer'*[5]. Thus Robert was exposed to volatile discussions in a highly charged atmosphere. Significantly, another observer noted: *'Trevithick sat with Robert on his knee many a night while talking to his father and it was through him, Robert was made an engineer'.*[6]

Then tragedy struck a few months later in August 1805. Robert's newly born sister did not survive and was buried in Longbenton graveyard. The following spring his mother also died. George Stephenson felt as if he had *'to tread the journey of life alone'.*[7] It was a terrible blow to him and he long lamented his bereavement. Devastated, he chose to forget by accepting a job in Montrose, Scotland, leaving his young son to be cared for by a twenty year old housekeeper Ann Snaith. During his absence Robert's uncle and namesake became a frequent visitor to Paradise Row. He and Ann married in March 1808, taking 'Bobby' to their new home. This long period of separation from a dominant father at a crucial time of his development may well have given Robert a streak of independence that would serve him well in the future.

No news was good news during George Stephenson's absence. To find his son happily settled with another family caused both guilt pangs and jealousy. He was *'angry'*[8] and in this mood *'recovered the possession of his child'.*[8] Two other unforeseen blows cost George Stephenson most of his hard earned savings while in Scotland. His father had lost his eyesight from a blast of steam; unable to work, he had accumulated debts of about £15. George

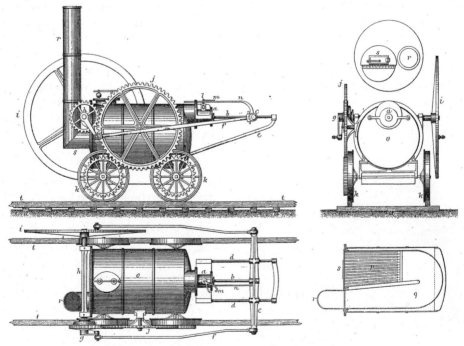

Trevithick's Gateshead Locomotive 1805

now took on the mantle of patriarch, paid off the money owed and moved his parents to a comfortable cottage adjoining the waggonway near to his own home, keeping them for the rest of their lives. Having doting grandparents close at hand added another dimension to young Robert's life. *'Old Bob'*[9] undoubtedly indulged his grandson with tales by his fireside which inspired the imagination of a young mind.

George Stephenson's renewed confidence in the face of adversity becomes evident. In 1808, *'Lord Castlereagh carried a measure for the establishment of a local militia of 200,000 men'*[10] for the continuing war with France. Riots broke out in large industrial towns such as Newcastle and Manchester. On being drawn for the army George did not rebel, but paid another man to *'go a-soldiering'*[10] in his stead. Undaunted he set up a contracting business together with Robert Weatherburn and George Dodds in order to maintain low pressure pumping and winding engines both at West Moor pit and elsewhere; *'they divided the work amongst them... the average earnings of each amounting to, from 18s to 20s a week'.*[11] The elder Stephenson soon earned himself a reputation locally as an engine doctor.

A new housekeeper also had to be found. The first choice proved unsatisfactory, so Aunt Nelly Stephenson became another substitute mother: *'It was a bright day for little Robert when this young woman entered the cottage at West Moor'.*[12] Three years younger than George, Eleanor had a serious disposition and was often thwarted by the antics of her charge. Described as a mischievous lad, Robert could be cheeky after a gill of mild beer *'and astounded his relatives by asserting that his staid aunt could not pass an ale house without entering it'.*[13] In fact Aunt Nelly offered light relief to a dominant father, who had a determination to be ambitious for his clever son, *'now growing up a healthy, intelligent boy... possessing an abundant capacity for knowledge'.*[14]

'Robert must wark, wark, as I hae warked afore him'.[15] Accordingly, when he did attend primary school in Longbenton run by the parish clerk Tommy Rutter, *'George's chief injunction to his only child'*[16] was not only to *'mind the buikes'*[16] but to work for a living. Like his father before him, young Robert had to carry miners picks from West Moor to Longbenton smith's shop, leave them to be sharpened then collect them after school. Thus heavily laden *'Aunt Nelly used to pity her bairn for having to trudge so far, to and fro'*[17].

To achieve the coveted post of enginewright, George Stephenson continued to spend most of his leisure time pursuing an understanding of the engines under his care. Every weekend he took one part of it to pieces in order to improve its mechanism and at the same time understand its action. Robert's earliest recollections were sitting on his father's knee watching his brows knit over difficult points, *'hammer in hand...marking*

Rutter's School, Longbenton

the deftness and precision with which his right hand plied its craft[18] …with *'indomitable perseverance'.*[19]

The Stephensons' living room was full of intriguing apparatus and Robert's environment proved to be the main source of his education. Making model engines of clay, the constant chat about this mechanical problem and that issue arising at the colliery was an everyday occurrence. Inevitably George brought an emotional pressure to bear upon

Trevithick's visiting card

an indulged son. And so *'to help father then and ever after became young Robert's proudest moments'.*[20] Indeed, he later declared: *'I have attended to machinery all of my life'.*[21] This was not an exaggeration. His earliest recollections were to assist his father; for instance when setting up an engine *'at the Ochre Quarry to pump it dry, he was scarcely absent for an hour'*[20] and had the audacity to call an engineman *'a fool',*[22] such was the extent of his practical knowledge.

Reflecting on this time Robert Stephenson realised that poverty could be considered as a *'mother of invention'.*[23] He would vividly remember how the shortage of horses during the Peninsular campaign almost brought the mining industry to a halt. Stockpiles of coal placed the mine owners under pressure to adopt the locomotive as a realistic alternative to the horse and set their engineers to the task.

Trevithick had not entirely given up demonstrating his high-pressure engine on wheels. In order to win a wager, Richard Trevithick's *Catch-me-who-can*[24] ran on a temporary circular track near to Euston Square, London during the summer of 1808. Constructed by the engineer John Rastrick at Hazeldine & Co., the locomotive became the first passenger engine. The spectators, who paid a shilling a ride, experienced a future railway in miniature. Realising that the momentum of the machine alone would enable the wheels and cranks to be carried over the dead centre, Trevithick abandoned the flywheel. This locomotive with single driving wheels, achieved a speed of fifteen miles an hour on a curved track. It attracted many engineers and colliery owners from the north of England including John Buddle, William Stobart and Charles Brandling. Doubtless, they returned home with Trevithick's visiting card in their pocket, depicting the simple design with an exhaust pipe used to stimulate the fire, thus providing a constant supply of steam.

Not surprisingly, when Charles Brandling decided to mechanise his waggonway from Middleton Colliery across Hunslet Moor to the staithes at Leeds, his agent John Blenkinsop had a Trevithick-type locomotive in mind. He commissioned Matthew Murray to construct the motive power for his rack and pinion track. This experienced and innovative mechanical engineer was able to set two vertical cylinders on to a wrought iron boiler and produce a sound, working machine.

If George Stephenson was to play a part in this sudden demand for locomotives, he needed

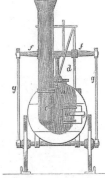
Trevithick's 'Catch-me-who-can' 1808

a position. Fortuitously, Nicholas Wood became an apprentice to the Killingworth viewer Ralph Dodds during the spring of 1811. Being young and impressionable, Wood got to know George well and admired his determination to succeed.

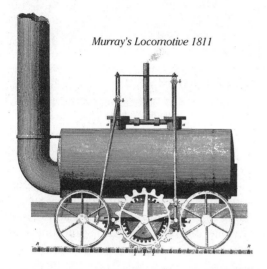

Murray's Locomotive 1811

By chance, the colliery enginewright William McCree lived next door to the Stephensons and George *'frequently discussed matters relating to machinery and the steam engine and he always thought he knew more of the principles of the steam engine than his superior'.*[25] McCree must have felt vulnerable and defended his position with long and heated arguments. Dodds eventually allowed the relentlessly persuasive George Stephenson to *'carry out his nostrums… much to the chagrin of McCree, the master enginewright'.*[25] Young Robert therefore appreciated the value of constructive discussions over a long period of time if the argument was soundly based by a committed person. After the elder Stephenson had proved his point and the pit worked more efficiently, he became a financial asset to the owners: Earl Strathmore, Sir Thomas Liddell and the Rt. Hon. James Stuart-Wortley-Mackenzie. Called the *'Grand Allies'*[26] they were the largest mining consortium in Great Britain. In fact George Stephenson superseded McCree in all but name, the latter being reduced to a menial

job. In April 1812, McCree suffered a fatal accident at the pit and Stephenson became the Killingworth enginewright with a salary. Soon his son would be party to exhaustive critical scrutiny concerning the efforts of locomotive pioneers.

At Wylam, Christopher Blackett revived an interest in locomotives. On being given a second chance to supply the colliery owner with one, Trevithick refused. Both he and his chief mechanic Steele preferred to serve the war effort in London. Consequently an attempt to plagiarise the Cornishman's design failed. With the help of Wylam's chief enginewright, a Trevithick-type locomotive with a single cylinder and flywheel was constructed by Tommy Waters at Pipewellgate in 1812. Due to a lack of power it did not perform well on the Wylam plate *'Railroad'.*[27] Hugh Taylor recalled how in 1812 together with Wood and Stephenson examined this locomotive: *'There was no idea that the machine would be sufficiently adhesive to the rails by the action of its own weight; but I remember a man going before - and scattering ashes on the rails, in order to give it adhesiveness'.*[28] But Blackett *'persevered with his experiments'*[29] and encouraged his highly ingenious viewer William Hedley to design his own version. Two were built at Wylam over the winter of 1812/13, the *Puffing Billy* and *Wylam Dilly*; both ran well. Perhaps to avoid paying royalties, Hedley departed from previous designs by adopting a 'grasshopper' motion and also positioning the cylinders on either side of the boiler. A close friend of the enginewright Jonathon Forster, George Stephenson was a keen observer and *'resolved to make himself thoroughly acquainted'*[30] with every move, flaunting *'his conviction that a much more effective engine might be made'.*[30] It is inconceivable that nine-year-old Robert did not accompany his father and Nicholas Wood on their frequent visits to Wylam.

On the afternoon of 2 September 1813, one of Matthew Murray's locomotives made a debut as part of Blenkinsop's rack & pinion patent[31] system on the Kenton & Coxlodge waggonway which served Charles Brandling's pits in the North East. Brandling even provided an excellent dinner served on a 'Grand Stand' especially erected for this prestigious occasion. In typical fashion George Stephenson declared that *'he could make a better engine than that, to go upon legs'.*[32] The ingenuity of Brunton's patent obviously impressed him, but fortunately he was persuaded to follow mainstream precedents, and his brother Robert's position as *'Engineman'*[33] enabled opportunities for close scrutiny. Still at Tommy Rutter's school with time to spare, ten-year old Robert would have the chance of exciting rides on a system that was considered by many to be the best mechanical replacement for horse traction waggonways.

Not to be outdone, the Grand Allies gave every encouragement to their viewer Ralph Dodds, under-viewer Nicholas Wood and enginewright George Stephenson to provide a travelling engine for the Killingworth waggonway. Like Murray's locomotive in every way with one exception: by necessity it had flanged wheels to run on the smooth rails. The decision to retain the cast iron railway may have been to save money as the Blenkinsop rack & pinion rail was expensive. During the ten months construction time, there was much *'anxiety and frequent alterations to the parts'.*[34] Robert Stephenson recalled that his

Puffing Billy 1813

father questioned the possibility of adhesion and *'caused a number of workmen to mount upon the wheels of a wagon moderately loaded and throw their entire weight upon the spokes on one side'.*[34] Over the next ten years, the budding engineer Robert Stephenson came to appreciate the value of team spirit: one major reason for his success.

On seeing that the wagon did move forwards, smooth wheels were adopted following Trevithick's precedent at Pipewellgate in 1805. Described as a somewhat *'cumbrous and clumsy'*[34] locomotive, it was first tried at the Killingworth waggonway on 25 July 1814; another source states *Blucher* proved a nuisance to the neighbourhood as the steam was allowed to escape from the sides of the engine. The slowness of its tractive power presented little, if any, advantage in point of economy over horse power.

Despite *'considerable derangement to the machinery',*[34] due to a lack of springs and jerks of the cogwheels, a modification did not take place until the following year. A continuous

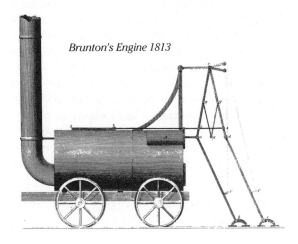

Brunton's Engine 1813

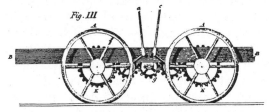

Blucher's spur wheels 1814

chain which rolled over indented wheels placed on the centre of each axle and was so arranged that the two pairs of wheels were effectively coupled, replacing the cogwheels. This change induced Dodds and Stephenson to take out a patent on 28 February 1815. But the chain had already been adopted by another enterprising pioneer, consequently Nicholas Wood wrote in his Memorandum Notebook: *'from these unlucky circumstances, they have made the patent null and of no use'.*[35] Possibly as compensation, the Grand Allies gave George a rise to £100 a year; he was after all the driving force in the team, with the others making valuable contributions. Although associated with Killingworth, this locomotive was actually built at the Longbenton smithy. Twenty guineas were contributed by the Grand Allies *'as a gratuity for the removal of the machine'*[36] to Killingworth on 18 March 1815.

Fully aware that Robert had inherited his own inventive flair, George made the child an object of an ambition to be *'a skilful engineer and a perfect man of business'*[37] though there were two obstacles: *'his ignorance of mathematics and his inability to write with facility or logical exactness'.*[37] Realistically, the elder Stephenson knew that within the mining industry he could not aspire to be a viewer. *'What he desired to be himself, that he also wished his son to be. Robert Stephenson should be an engineer and a director of labour'.*[37]

So on 14 August 1815, Robert became a day pupil at the Percy Street Academy, Newcastle upon Tyne, instead of the Grammar School. Mathematics was taught by the headmaster John Bruce, a friend of Dr Charles Hutton, author of significant scientific publications. Instead of flourishing at the school, Robert's fellow pupils *'failed to detect in him any remarkable signs of talent, and at the time of his death some still expressed their astonishment at his scientific acquirements and professional achievements'.*[37] He stood out in this middle-class crowd with his homemade clothes, hob-nailed boots which clattered on the floor and packed lunch of rye bread. Although he withstood the bullying silently, his suffering must have had a profound effect at an impressionable age. As a means of self-preservation he escaped from the playground by going to his uncle's for lunch and became a reading member at the nearby Literary & Philosophical Society.

'During the time Robert attended school in Newcastle, his father made the boy's education instrumental to his own'.[38] In order to discover the latest steam engine developments and scientific achievements, he was allowed to borrow from the Lit. & Phil. Society *'standard popular works and encyclopaedic volumes of natural science and inventions such as "Repertory of Arts & Sciences".'*[38] A secretary

Dr Bruce's Percy Street Academy

of the Society, the cheerful Rev. William Turner soon befriended the teenager, who later recalled his *'valuable assistance and instruction'*.[39] At home, father and son studied together. Robert was compelled to read out loud *'but the labour went very much against the boy's grain'*. [40] Valuable books had to remain in the library. So Robert taught himself the art of translating information into a diagrammatic format for his father's benefit.

One instance of turning scientific reading into practice has been recorded. After studying Franklin's description of the lightning experiment Robert spent his savings at a brazier's shop in Newcastle on half a mile of copper wire insulated with a few feet of silk chord and then made a large kite, which he flew in a meadow opposite his home in Paradise Row. When the kite came down on the backs of the cows, they danced in all directions with upright tails. The experiment certainly worked, with his father chuckling with pride while waiting at the cottage with his horse. When the scientific trick also knocked his horse to the ground, George was not amused: *'You mischeevous scoondrel - aal pall thee.'*[41] Robert did not wait to be beaten. Out of school activities provided the stimulus for an inventive mind.

After a few months at school, the Rev. Turner provided Robert *'with books, with instruments and with council'*[39] on a project culminating in fame. Ever since the Felling Colliery explosion of 1812 killing ninety men and boys, George Stephenson had turned his fertile mind to developing a practical safety lamp for miners. As a consequence of the formation of the coal measures, methane gas accumulated in the deepest mines and Killingworth was particularly dangerous. Legend has it that the shaft sinker Kit Hepple appealed to George's sense of economy. Disruption to productivity due to a huge loss of life was worse than machinery breakdown; *'the price of coal mining now is pitmen's lives'*.[42] How right Hepple was. Both mine workers and owners would be eternally grateful. For three years George's numerous attempts failed. Nicholas Wood added *'without going into unnecessary details of all his schemes which he communicated to me... all of which proved abortive'*.[43]

When a South Shields committee invited the eminent scientist Sir Humphrey Davy to produce a successful lamp resulting in a visit to North East collieries on 24 August 1815, George Stephenson's sense of competition induced him to act. Nor did he find it difficult to rally an enthusiastic force. His prodigious child was in a position to borrow equipment from the Literary & Philosophical Society and seek advice from the Rev. Turner while Nicholas Wood's education, training and position ensured the realisation of the Killingworth miner's safety lamp.

An earlier incident gave them a well-known theory to work on. By building a wall at the pit's mouth and restricting atmospheric air, a potentially dangerous fire had been put out. They must solve the problem of containing the flame within the protective glass of an oil lamp.

Wood prepared the drawings and conducted the experiments within their empirical approach. If methane gas and atmospheric air were admitted through the bottom of the lamp, it would burn safely within the flame zone restricted by a perforated top which prevented atmospheric air reaching the flame from above. The correct velocity and proportions had to be discovered.

The team worked exceptionally quickly within a three-month period; both senior men had time-consuming jobs and young Robert's schooldays were taxing as well, with a ten mile a day return journey even though he sometimes rode on a donkey. *'After several evenings careful deliberations'*,[44] a drawing of their intentions was produced. Wood explained the sequence of events:

'turning my thoughts towards a more simple contrivance I found that Hydrogen Gas ascending thro' narrow Tubes on being lighted at the End,

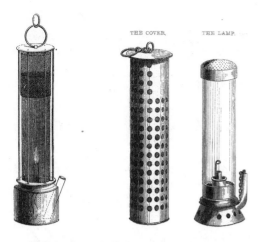

THE COVER.   THE LAMP.

Miners Lamps: the Davy and the Geordie

the Fire never descended the Tube. I therefore ordered a Lamp to be made with the Flame covered by a Glass and to be supply'd with Air thro a small Tube $^3/_{16}$ in diameter.... now it is next to impossible for the above Lamp to Fire the Hydrogen Gas on the outside of it. The Flame in the inside is burning more Air than the Tube would contain did it not issue thro' with a great Velocity - thereby effectually keeping the Flame from descending the Tube'.[45]

The experiments took place at Wood's house where they experienced a serious accident; 'the receiver blew up, first to the ceiling of the house and then fell into atoms'.[46] Robert would have some explaining to do. Undeterred, they continued by constructing a deal box with windows of glass instead. Wood recorded how the first lamp was not made according to his precise drawing and measurements. Despite a stopper, the tube was too large and the lamp went out during the trial. Wood denied dangerous conditions: 'we had had sufficient experience not to employ more gas than was necessary; at most an explosion might have burned the hands of the operator'.[46]

Clearly more air was needed. The altered lamp had three small tubes and although the flame improved it was not yet up to expectations. If holes were made in the metal base 'placed at

a distance from each other, equal to the length of the tubes, the air would get in better, and the effect in preventing the communication of explosion would be the same.'[45]

This version was a success. After repeated trials 'it never fired the surrounding gas but burnt in the midst of it with perfect safety'.[45] On Friday 17 November Wood displayed the lamp before local mine owners, including the Brandling brothers. Being a marketable product, if proprietors could be persuaded that each miner should be equipped with a lamp, the enterprise would prove profitable. Indeed the Grand Allies later imposed a 'penalty of half-a-crown'[47] on all miners under their employment if they did not use it.

Wood stated: 'On Tuesday night Decr. 5th we laid it before the Literary & Philosophical Society in Newcastle, when it was thought by all present to be the most useful and most simple one yet...'[45] Shortly afterwards, Davy's lamp was also received and exhibited to Newcastle coal miners. By investigating the properties of gas, the scientist discovered that the methane would not pass through small tubes and designed a lamp of fine wire gauze. Again the flame would be restricted unless the gauze reached an extremely high temperature, and then it would ignite. The eminent scientist's solution to provide a light in a dangerous area was therefore only partial. And pipped to the post, accusations of plagiarism followed. An indignant Sir Humphrey reacted strongly. How could a person without any knowledge of the elements of chemistry produce a successful lamp? The elder Stephenson became a catalyst for its promotion and the lamp was known affectionately as the 'Geordie'.[48]

'To George Stephenson the best consequences of his invention was the quarrel which it provoked between his friends and the supporters of Sir Humphrey Davy. The coal owners of the district formed themselves into two parties. A newspaper war was waged, in which the advocates of Stephenson were altogether victorious.'[49]

Robert's letter during miner's lamp controversy

The Stephensons now enjoyed a high-profile image and respect among local magnates, notably the Brandling brothers and William Losh, owner of a chemical factory and partner of the iron foundry Losh, Wilson & Bell. Helping to produce a successful miners' safety lamp was Robert Stephenson's first encounter with national fame. An idea translated into reality. And acting as his father's scribe during the drawn out newspaper controversy with Sir Humphrey, gave him the experience of written argument and this involvement with a long-standing war of words would not be his last. The events of 1815 also kindled a life-long fascination with chemistry. In 1851 a published statement records: *'Robert Stephenson believes his knowledge in chemistry to surpass his attainments in engineering'.*[50]

The influence of William Losh

William Losh was Robert Stephenson's introduction to the outside world. Having been educated on the continent, *'this highly cultivated gentleman'*[51] studied metallurgy in Sweden and chemistry in Paris. The gift of a sundial drawing from the ardent youth with a sincere interest in science was gratefully received. Using Ferguson's well-known astronomy book, Robert had been set a summer holiday activity by his father to construct a sundial. He argued *'I had not learnt sufficient astronomy and mathematics to do the necessary calculations. But he would have no denial'.*[52] In the same way George encouraged competitive sports, and thus stretched both mentally and physically to the limits, Robert would then take the necessary leap into the dark.

Robert's sundial

The thirteen year old endured many mental agonies doing the calibrations to adapt the dial to Killingworth's latitude. Then together father and son hewed, carved and polished the stone with the date MDCCCXVI and placed it

Dial Cottage, West Moor. Home to George and Robert Stephenson 1805-23

over the new front door to their home, renamed *'Dial Cottage'*. George had built an extension which included the luxury of a staircase instead of a ladder, another living room and bedroom above.

During the next month William Losh and George Stephenson applied for a railway patent including rail, wheel and engine improvements. Experiments to ascertain the strength of metals in order to produce two types of wheel, cast iron rail and half-lap joints intended to alleviate irregularities, were all conducted under Losh's expert eye. Robert's interest in metal properties almost certainly stemmed from this time. These were heady days before the limitations of scientific theory. The philosophies of Humboldt and others known to Losh would have had an impact on a young impressionable mind. Anything was possible.

By 1816, there was a reluctance by colliery owners to invest further funding into locomotive development; the war was over, the crisis passed, horses and fodder had become plentiful again. But George Stephenson still had one more locomotive order to fulfil for the Duke of Portland, owner of the Kilmarnock & Troon Railway. In order to increase the steam generating capacity, he simply made the locomotive larger with an enormous chimney and spread the weight by adding another axle. A contemporary artist gave a graphic description: *'The carcase sat on three pairs of wheels... which were turned... like so many grindstones'.*[53] By incorporating steam springs into the Patent Specification, it was hoped to improve the machine's performance. In practice this contrivance proved ineffective due to the locomotive's inability to maintain a constant supply of high-pressure steam. Consequently, the six-wheeled locomotive more often than not rode 'solid' resulting in broken rails to the extent that horses were re-introduced on this line.

The initial failure of this locomotive to fulfil its function may well have caused the elder Stephenson to contemplate emigrating to the United States with his sister Ann, her husband John Nixon and young family. There seemed *'little prospect of introducing the locomotive into general use, so George Stephenson saw the germ of a great revolution in navigation'.*[54] His intrinsic knowledge lay with Newcomen and Watt-type stationary engines and his motivation lay with the business prospects of adopting these low-pressure steam machines for whatever

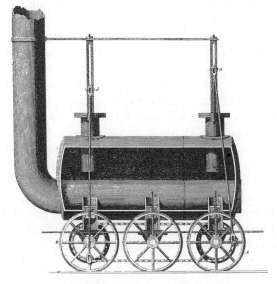

Losh and Stephenson's Locomotive 1816

was feasible at the time. His partner for the 'good speculation'[54] was to be John Burrell, the iron founder. A generation younger, Robert's enthusiasm lay with the locomotive.

A railway engineer

At a dinner held in the Stephensons' honour, George recalled how his son Robert:

'became my assistant and my companion… and at nights we worked together at engineering. I got leave to go from Killingworth to lay down a railway at Hetton and next to Darlington…'[55]

In 1819 the prosperous Hetton Coal Company determined to have an eight-mile waggonway transformed into a *'Railway'*,[56] George Stephenson accepted the post of *'consulting engineer'*[56] and he was able to order cast-iron rails, chairs and locomotives according to the Losh / Stephenson patent[57] of 1816. For the first time there would be a profit from the patentee's efforts; this must have been a major deciding factor against emigrating to the New World. He also continued to be a consultant enginewright travelling extensively in the district. Undoubtedly Robert welcomed the opportunity to consolidate concepts from books absorbed over the last four years and put these ideas into practice. Although close friendships were eventually formed, school was not particularly conducive. On leaving the Academy in June 1819, his father arranged extra *'mathematical tuition lessons with Mr Riddell'*[58] and an apprenticeship to Nicholas Wood as an under-viewer. Robert's training included administration, surveying, tunnel construction, being in charge of engines and track both underground and to the staith; as well as engineering, an understanding of physical chemistry and geology were also important. The investigative aspects of this work would appeal to the practical teenager.

Only once a fortnight did Robert Stephenson go down the mine with his master, still an under-viewer at Killingworth. Punctual to the minute, he met Wood at 9 o'clock and they descended the mine in the course of their inspection duties to ensure efficient production. For the rest of the working week and during much of his leisure time, he assisted with engineering matters concerning his father's numerous railway-associated contracts and mine ownership.

Everyone in the mining industry provided their own equipment and the young engineer designed his own instruments including an unusually large mining compass. The proud creator had the inscription *'Robert Stephenson fecit'*[59] engraved on the brass. Out of hours, he *'assisted in superintending the works of the Hetton railway'*,[60] working with his uncle Robert who had been appointed resident engineer. At least three locomotives would be required for this railway.

Robert Stephenson stated that: *'The locomotive engine, independent of the railways would be useless'*,[61] both had to improve together. Over the next five years he embarked on a serious study of metal properties for rail usage, locomotive construction and bridges. Initially, he went to look at the different types of rails used by colliery owners in the district and then further afield to Coalbrookdale: *'The most suitable type of iron for rails had formed the subject of frequent conversations between George Stephenson and his son in their cottage at Killingworth for many years'*.[62]

Being less brittle than cast-iron, some wrought iron rails were laid at Killingworth as early as 1815. Nicholas Wood commented that the use of wrought iron *'was much objected to at the time…on account of its being supposed to laminate'*.[63] The Stephensons produced a report in order to challenge this misconception: if the iron was of good quality and soundly manufactured it would stand the test of time. George's *'intimate friend'*[64] John Birkinshaw, an agent of the Bedlington Iron Company, was encouraged by his manager Michael Longridge to take out a patent for a wrought iron rail. Sections of rail were considered as a beam and a fish-bellied shape strengthened the fifteen-foot rail at its weakest point. Acting as his father's secretary until 1824, Robert wrote how the rails *'make a fine line for our engines, as there are so few joints'.*[65] The widespread adoption of this rail by colliery owners and railway companies would be extremely lucrative for those involved.

An event reveals Birkinshaw's close friendship with George Stephenson: when he signed the latter's marriage bond with Elizabeth Hindmarsh. *'He could now afford to indulge in romance'*[66] and for the second time George married in Newburn Parish Church on 29 March 1820. Robert was a witness. Recently he had experienced a significant change to the cosy close-knit Stephenson unit at Killingworth. Not long after his grandfather Stephenson died, he also lost his grandmother Mabel Stephenson in May 1818. Aunt Eleanor then left 'Dial Cottage' and now a new matriarch was installed. On the surface, a polite Robert Stephenson responded well. His stepmother introduced social graces, encouraging him to play the flute and be a member of the Longbenton Church Orchestra.

Another projected local line, this time a public railway, was about to receive the royal assent and lay within the elder Stephenson's grasp. *'One day in 1821, Edward Pease was writing in his room when a servant announced that two strangers wished to speak to him'.*[67] Accompanied by Nicholas Wood, George Stephenson went to Darlington *'for the purpose of soliciting Mr Edward Pease, the chief projector of the new line, to secure for him the job of making of the railroad'.*[68] Wood later confirmed how they travelled by coach on their own initiative to Stockton; *'then we had a walk of twelve miles through the fields over the line of the proposed railway'.*[69] The practical straightforward approach of the elder Stephenson appealed to Pease's business instincts. Cost cuts on the planned line were offered in all aspects of the railway's construction. Only after the Stockton & Darlington Railway (S&DR) Act was incorporated on 19 April 1821 did George receive confirmation of his post *'as the Company's engineer'.*[70] Diplomatic letters written by Robert on his father's behalf helped to secure the confidence of other S&DR directors.

News travelled fast, and the railway visionary William James came to Tyneside during the summer of 1821 with the distinct intention of viewing the various types of locomotives and adopting them for his projected public railways. Ever since he had seen Trevithick's road carriage at Camborne, Cornwall in 1803, James' constant endeavour was to find an engine capable of being converted into a locomotive of sufficient power to obtain high speeds. From 1820 onwards, he printed publications advocating a railway network powered by locomotives for passenger as well as mineral traffic. After his visit to Killingworth, an immediate friendship blossomed between the passenger train advocate and Robert Stephenson. The latter would have read about national rail network schemes from other enthusiasts but their promotion had been for freight with different demands. Almost certainly before meeting James, Robert's only desire was to create an efficient locomotive acceptable to colliery owners as a replacement for the horse on railways projected by his father's consultancy business. William James wished to establish a fast and cheap service for people whereby *'space is nearly destroyed'*[71]. The senior man soon became an admired mentor of the young locomotive enthusiast. And Robert Stephenson came to appreciate that if his attempts to convince his stubborn father of technical improvements and necessary changes concerning railway construction continued to fail, William James could be persuaded.

According to an eye-witness, heated discussions occurred between father and son, *'more especially with reference to the growing powers of the locomotive engine. The son was even more enthusiastic than the father on this subject. Robert would suggest alterations and improvements in this, that, and the other details* of the machine. His father, on the contrary, would offer every possible objection defending the existing arrangements'.[72]

That George Stephenson adamantly opposed some of his son's intentions, until he was proved undeniably wrong, can be considered in a positive light. In order to convince his father, Robert had to prove his point and not make any expensive mistakes. The challenge encouraged him to focus on one development and then another.

Undoubtedly aware of published articles about the steam engine, Robert would be familiar with the drawing of Trevithick's high-pressure engine of 1803 as adapted to a locomotive, published in Rees 'Cyclopaedia'.[73] From Charles Brandling, he may also have seen Trevithick's card of Catch-me-who-can. Both depict the application of the blast to stimulate the fire; by adopting Trevithick's expedient of conveying the exhaust steam into the chimney, so stimulated the draught from the fire as to increase the generation of steam and with it the engine's power of traction. Robert Stephenson considered the blast to be 'a most important consequence to railway communication...the

success of the locomotive depended upon its adoption'.[74] Following Trevithick's precedent, he placed the exhaust pipe from the cylinder into the chimney at right angles just above the boiler, allowing the steam to escape in a vertical direction and consequently increasing the draught creating an 'intensity of combustion in the furnace'.[74] He called this blast action a 'simple but beautiful expedient'[74] and added, 'the experiment was no sooner made than the power of the engine was at once doubled... without in any way adding to its weight'[74]. Now his father's six-wheeled locomotive could be reduced to four wheels; the 1816 locomotive sent to Scotland had failed due to excessive weight. From his future actions and statements, it is possible to conclude that George disapproved of Robert's adoption of the blast on economic grounds. Nevertheless George was proud 'of his son's suggestions and often warmed and excited by his brilliant anticipations of the ultimate triumph of the locomotive'.[72]

A two-axle showpiece locomotive was constructed at the West Moor engine workshop during the summer of 1821, and even though George objected to this coal-eating machine, it did not contravene the 1816 patent and could

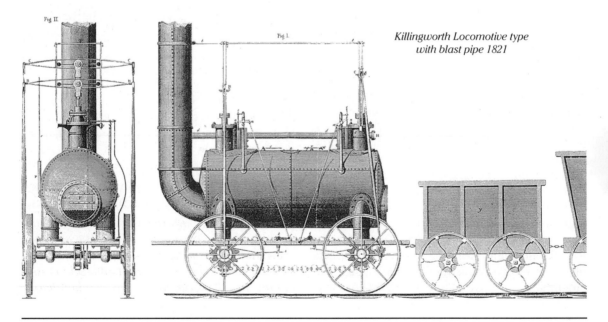

Killingworth Locomotive type
with blast pipe 1821

still be considered as his, though other commentators realised the significance of Robert's initiative at this time. A signed partnership with James gave the possibility of being involved in more railway projects. On the crest of an ambitious wave, George would astonish everyone. Indeed Killingworth became a mecca for colliery engineers and railway promoters, among them Edward Pease. In order to emphasise the *'economy'* of the travelling engine, George Stephenson reputedly showed him the colliery books. On 2 August 1821, the Tyneside viewer William Stobart expressed his opinion: *'the last and best Locomotive Engine of Mr. George Stephenson built is certainly a wonderful piece of machinery'*[75]. Having spent a day at Killingworth, Stobart goes on to say how the elder Stephenson boasted about going to *'Warwickshire on either tomorrow or Wednesday morning…his business is upon a long railway of about 100 miles and Engines to suit'.*[75] What was called the Central Junction Railway had already been projected by James.

Robert Stephenson was extremely fortunate to have a teacher of Nicholas Wood's calibre. Wood taught his apprentice that systematic experiment was essential before arriving at a conclusion. With the objective of making the locomotive a more efficient working proposition, the simple and effective slide-valve, as perfected by Murray, was introduced to distribute the steam instead of the rotary cock. Being a technical and economical step forward, the slide-valve was actuated by a slip eccentric on each axle, with the eccentrics driving the valves by means of rods and bell cranks.[76]

Realising the necessity of training locomotive engineers, it was during 1821 that Robert singled out mining mechanics to specialise in the workshop. Indeed, William Hutchinson was to remain in his service for many years. On 2

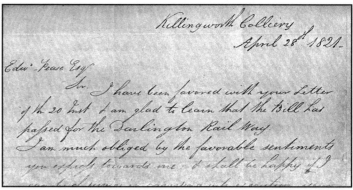

Letter to Edward Pease, 28 April 1821, written by Robert signed by George.

May 1845 he reminded his master *'I have now served you twenty-four years, the best part of my life-time'.*[77] Also the requisite machinery or specialist tools did not yet exist. Robert stressed that only accuracy of workmanship would produce a *'perfect action of the engine'.*[78] Construction of three Hetton locomotives had yet to begin and hopefully more would be required for the Stockton & Darlington Railway.

With the prospect of time-consuming engineering work both practical and theoretical, Robert Stephenson would have to abort his apprenticeship. Assisting his father as 'engineer'[79] on the Stockton & Darlington Railway, he joined the surveying team during the autumn of 1821. Another Act of Parliament would be required for George Stephenson's proposed change of route. Edward Pease's son Joseph remembered the *'slight spare bronzed boy'*[80] and how Robert won his argument with his father: *'in a barely intelligible Northumbrian brogue …by the respectful mention of Mr Bruce's opinions…to the authority of a worthy schoolmaster, George Stephenson invariably paid marked, almost superstitious, homage.'*[80]

Robert Stevenson in Edinburgh, the engineer of lighthouse fame and grandfather of the author Robert Louis Stevenson, had been retained as consultant engineer to the Stockton & Darlington Railway. His younger Killingworth namesake recorded one exhilarating

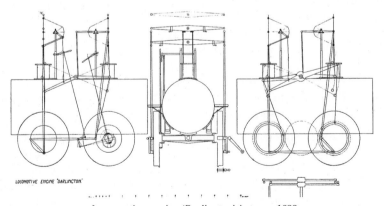

Contract specification for the S&DR written by Robert, April 1822.

discussion with him, and more visits to the consultant in Edinburgh almost certainly took place. From there the teenager wrote to a Durham colliery owner on 26 September 1821, recommending wrought iron for a proposed railway: *'His opinion on the point was clear and explicit, Robert was only eighteen years old at the time, but the letter is full of practical information... indicating habits of careful observation and the action of a vigorous and well disciplined intellect'.*[81]

In fact, most of the known Stockton & Darlington Railway documents from April 1821 until May 1824 associated with the Stephensons are in Robert's hand, including a four-page estimate of anticipated revenues. The detailed contracts and reports are evidence of his capabilities and his conviction that to employ independent contractors was the fairest and best method of railway construction. That Stockton & Darlington Railway contractors were asked to report to him at Killingworth in April 1822, indicates a permanent presence at the workshop and therefore still constructing the Hetton locomotives. Officially Robert Stephenson was not employed at the colliery any more.

For the engineering work on the Stockton &

Darlington Railway, George gave his son credit. Was he in danger of losing a major asset? During the late summer of 1822, Robert Stephenson went to work for William James in order to help with the Liverpool to Manchester railway survey. This was an opportunity to gain experience and broaden his horizons. Robert Stephenson's letters to James show how he attempted to influence the far-sighted man. A passenger railway network would demand an efficient, uninterrupted service requiring a single reliable motive power on a safe track. He advised not to have a *'fixed engine'*[82] on the Liverpool to Manchester railway and a few weeks later wrote... *'lay a strong railway down and enjoy the advantage of Locomotive Engines (for no doubt they are an advantage over every other mode hitherto used)'.*[82] So certain was Robert Stephenson of his convictions, his letters have an air of arrogance.

George Stephenson needed his son's services again and recalled Robert to the North East: *'I am very much in want of Robert, you will send him off as soon as possible as I want him to go to Knaresburgh [sic] and also do business on the Darlington Railway'*[83]. There was power in absence and the locomotive enthusiast was now able to influence his father

Locomotive engine 'Darlington' Autumn 1822

regarding design changes to the locomotive engine for 'DARLINGTON',[84] even though these improvements contravened the 1816 patent. Describing his locomotive design intentions as conceived but not entirely implemented at Killingworth, Robert Stephenson stated that they were the *'germ of all that has since been effected...in fact could be regarded as the type of the present locomotive engine'.*[85] He explained how *'the chain after a few years used to become stretched, and then the engines were liable to irregularity in their working forward again. The chain was laid aside and the front and hind wheels were united by rods on the outside, instead of by rods and cranks axles inside as specified in the original patent. This expedient completely answered the purpose required, without involving any expensive or difficult workmanship'.*[85 & 86]

On trial with an existing Killingworth locomotive it would be discovered that to combine the connecting rods with the crosshead and the slide bar demanded a high degree of precision. As George Stephenson's steam springs did not function as intended however ingenious they appeared to the observer, Robert substituted a pivoted axle to accommodate an uneven track; this precluded the loose eccentrics being on each axle.

Robert Stephenson summarised the essential components for a prototype locomotive: *'simple and direct communication between the cylinders and the wheels...horizontal rods connecting the wheels...and finally, a beautiful method of exciting the combustion of the fuel by employing the waste steam, which had formerly been allowed uselessly to escape into the air'.*[85]

EDINBURGH and NEWCASTLE upon TYNE: 1822 - 1824

In late October 1822 Robert Stephenson attended Edinburgh University in order to learn more about *'the properties of gas to aid*

Robert's university prize description, 1823

his experiments with the object of improving the locomotive engine'[1]. Despite George's comparative wealth at this time, his father had to be persuaded by the argument of an *'imperative duty'*[2] to allow a college education, later interpreted as a determination 'to furnish his son with as complete a scientific culture as his means would afford'.[3] Robert thoroughly enjoyed the interaction of ideas from his lecturers Dr Hope, Dr Murray, Professor Jameson and Professor John Leslie. He also found time to visit Robert Stevenson in connection with the Stockton & Darlington Railway and Robert Bald the distinguished mining engineer. Of the latter he recalled:

'Besides taking me with him to the meetings of the Royal & other societies, Mr Bald introduced me to a very agreeable family, relatives of his own... There I met Jenny... She was a bonny lass and I being very young and susceptible fairly fell in love with her'.[3]

Visits of geological interest also took place,

'Edinburgh being in the midst of a district of highly interesting geological formation'.[3] Professor Jameson encouraged the use of hammers and chisels to obtain specimens and taught his students 'habits of observation'.[3] On being given a mathematics prize, Robert significantly chose: 'Tracts on Mathematical and Philosophical Subjects' on 'The Theory of Bridges' and 'The Force of Gunpowder'[4] by Charles Hutton, late Professor of Mathematics at the Royal Military Academy, Woolwich published London 1812 in three volumes; a familiar work, almost certainly on John Bruce's bookshelf.

One session of six months 'taught him as much as is usually learnt in three years'.[5] He studied so intensely that the experience gave him the ability 'to teach himself'[6]; indeed laid 'the foundation for future instruction'.[6] Robert's student days were to be short lived, because once again George Stephenson needed his son's services.

A public appearance

During Robert's six-month absence in Scotland, the style and content of his father's letters changed. They have a very different emphasis reflecting the elder man's sincere belief as to the best method of future railway construction. Directly opposite to his son's ideas, he continued to promote a mixture of motive powers requiring centrally placed inclines for many years to come. This practice introduced on the Stockton & Darlington Railway proved to be seriously flawed, as what could be regarded as perfectly adequate for a mineral railway was not suitable for passengers: too many delays and too many disruptions resulted from stretched ropes and changeovers. George Stephenson's system was likened to a lot of fiddlers not playing in concert. Yet he sang the praises of his system as exhibited on the Hetton Railway, 'the Standing Engines is doing exceedingly well; they will deliver 300,000 Tons p. annum; and by laying a double Railway on the bank they will deliver twice that number'.[7] From another letter written to William James on 18 December 1822, the elder Stephenson's irritation at James' intention concerning an insertion of a passenger clause in the second Stockton & Darlington Railway Bill is obvious: 'I would be obliged to you if you could return the Darlington Railway Act of parliament with your alterations and remarks upon it'.[8]

As Robert Stephenson had played a major role and having been 'designated engineer',[9] he went to London and helped progress this second Bill through Parliament. Therefore he almost certainly curtailed his course for a week or so. His last known letter from Edinburgh is dated 11 April 1823, having already received his prize. Natural Philosophy finished on 18 April, which he probably attended, but not the last chemistry lecture on 27 April. He appears oblivious to the fact that his parents had moved to Eldon Place, Newcastle. As the Strathmore estate was causing problems with the Bill, his support would be required. On the last day of March, the elder Stephenson had written to William Locke, formerly in a managerial post at Walbottle pit when George was a fireman: 'I expect to be in London in the course of a fortnight or three weeks, when I shall do myself the pleasure of calling, either in going or coming'.[10]

Clearly events had moved faster than expected; there would not be time to call on Locke en route to Parliament. Being exposed to a parliamentary select committee must have been a nerve-wracking experience for a teenager. Robert later recalled one vivid nightmare at the time of his 'first public appearance'.[9] While seeing the sites of London, his father was especially taken with a menagerie in the Strand:

'… and nothing would satisfy George but he must go and tip the keeper and see the lion at large. The proposal only put Robert into a great state of agitation. "My father is sure to stroke the lion, or do something rash of that kind. He will be killed, and then what will become of our Bill?"'[11]

That night Robert dreamt how the lion could be tamed with number 263. He had been reading a book left open at that page before he went to sleep.

Elated with success when the Bill passed through both Houses, the Stephensons called at the Locke household in Barnsley. Having served an apprenticeship under William Stobart at Pelaw on the Tyne's south bank and under his own father, Joseph Locke was already an experienced mining engineer, able to survey, sink shafts, construct railways, tunnels and stationary engines, manage men and ensure profitable returns. It was arranged that the seventeen year old would join them in a new enterprise to manufacture locomotives and stationary engines for the Stockton & Darlington Railway. Three decades later *The Times* reported that Locke *'may be said to complete the Triumvirate of the engineering world'*[12].

Back in Newcastle upon Tyne, a meeting was held with Edward Pease and Michael Longridge to form a partnership accordingly. *'Having formed the highest estimate of Robert's abilities'*,[13] Longridge recalled a year later, *'It was against my wish they commenced engine Builders, but after they had begun, considering it beneficial to the Bedlington Iron Co... I offered to take part with them'*.[14]

Edward Pease later wrote in his diary how he had lent Robert £500 *'in order to serve a worthy youth'*.[15] Described as *'a thoughtful and sagacious man, ready in resources'* and *'could see a hundred years ahead'*,[16] the money allowed the nineteen year old to be an equal partner and working manager. Pease's cousin Thomas Richardson, also became an equal shareholder from the onset. But being very busy in London as an executive founder of the celebrated discount house of Richardson, Overend & Gurney, he did not sign the Agreement. The intention had probably been for shares of £500 each, but in the event all five partners paid £800. Pease complained to his cousin: *'so long as the 1600£ we were jointly to furnish was raised it was of no moment to them from whence it came'*.[17] Thomas Richardson also formed a *'high opinion'*[13] of young Robert's *'energy and capacity'*.[13] Thus by his conduct towards his business partners and their influential associates, Robert Stephenson gained their respect and confidence.

Managing partner of Robert Stephenson & Company

On 23 June 1823 a Memorandum of co-partnership for twenty one years from 31 May 1823 was signed by Robert and George Stephenson, Edward Pease and Michael Longridge *'for carrying on the business of Engine Builders'*.[18] They would trade under the name of Robert Stephenson & Co. (RS&Co.) It was to be an engine factory like many others, but the first with the intention to specialise in locomotive production. Robert later stated that the establishment was founded *'for me'*.[19] His experience as an engine builder at West Moor 1819-22 admirably suited him to the position of working manager and he brought his mechanic Hutchinson with him. All contemporary records and circumstantial evidence confirms this. Some of Robert's engineering colleagues realised that his considerable knowledge of metal properties and the manufacture of iron stemmed from being actively and prominently involved in locomotive construction as a youth. Other sources recognise in 1823, Robert Stephenson *'was already acquainted with locomotive development because he had carried out improvements in the Killingworth and other locomotives'*.[20]

A fast developing industrial area in the vicinity of Forth Street, Newcastle upon Tyne was chosen for the new factory, situated in the south-eastern extremity of the cul-de-sac South Street and adjacent to Burrell's Iron Foundry. A cottage was converted to an

*Robert Stephenson & Co engine 1823 - Stephenson Locomotive Society
(Newcastle Centre) - McDowell Trust Collection*

been declared bankrupt and suffered imprisonment. Robert Stephenson also sent a letter of sympathy to the engineer a few months later:

'It gives rise to feelings of true regret when I reflect on your situation; but yet a consolation springs up when I consider your persevering spirit will for ever bear you up in the arms of triumph... It is these thoughts and these alone that could banish from my soul feelings of despair for one; the respect I have for him can be easier conceived than described. Can I ever forget the advice you have afforded me in your last letters? and what a heavenly inducement you pointed before me at the close, when you said that attention and obedience to my dear father would afford me music at midnight'.[24]

office; demolition took place to make space for suitable workshop structures and a house for the stationary engine, before the factory could be totally operational. Robert Stephenson *'had to supervise the building operations, engage men, take orders, advise on contracts, draw plans, make estimates, keep the accounts, and in all matters great or small, govern the young establishment on his own responsibility'.[21]* Other engineering firms belonging to Robert Wilson and Robert Hawthorn were already established in the area. George Stephenson's former boss would inevitably be a competitor.

Later given the respectful title of *'Chief'*,[22] the managing partner's first task was to complete the RS&Co. stationary engine plans. The castings and component parts were done elsewhere; probably at Burrells where Robert would have to keep an eagle eye on the castings for the Gaunless Bridge, but definitely not at the iron founders Losh, Wilson & Bell. The latter partner Thomas Bell was already commiserating with William James; 'Newcastle upon Tyne, August 14th 1823... *'My partners and myself are extremely sorry to hear of your misfortunes'.[23]* James had

It would take time to accept William James' advice to be tolerant and obedient. Man lives best through his creativity and Robert would be faithful to his engineering convictions. To juxtapose standing his ground with being dutiful proved difficult. His intention was to see James later in September: *'My father and I set off for London on Monday next, the 1st on our way to Cork.... Our return will probably be about the time you wish me to be at Liverpool'.[24]* The meeting almost certainly did not take place, as the Stephensons returned via Bristol having successfully secured orders for RS&Co. in London and Ireland. During this time Robert wrote graphic letters to Michael Longridge:

'Dublin 10 September 1823:...'We hope by this time we have got our fortunes made safe with the Lord of Carlisle's agents. We have some hopes of some orders for steam engines for South America, in the Columbia [sic] State...

Cork 16 September 1823... when it [the mail

coach] stopped at the Post Office, to see four large cavalry pistols and two blunderbusses handed up to the guard... I can assure my father's courage was daunted, though I don't suppose he will confess with it...

We were very kindly received at the Dripsay Paper Works by Macnay's family, and have just finished our business with them for the present, and instead leaving Cork in the steam packet this day for Bristol. From there we shall make the best of our way to Shifnal [Coalbrookdale] in Shropshire and our business there will probably detain us five or six days. A small boiler will be wanted to send to Ireland.'[25]

By December the factory was almost fully operational and Joseph Locke soon found himself in a position of authority. From his letters to Robert written a few years later, it is clear that the two young engineers were exceptionally close, but the time spent together at the factory until April 1824 was fragmented and short lived.

Ever since his schooldays at Rutter's, Robert Stephenson had been stretched to the full and with the foundation of Robert Stephenson & Co. he had driven himself both mentally and physically; having to superintend every operation, the responsibility for a nineteen year-old must have been tremendous. Those close to him were aware of the strain caused by locomotive design constraints imposed by George Stephenson. Whether stationary engines or locomotives, Robert's aim was to simplify the design and he challenged his father about resorting to indirect drive in combination with outside rods connecting the wheels:

'They have removed the parallel motion... as they are found entirely superfluous... I have never seen one mathematically true, not even in principle - I have found since I left home that in every case where all the bars are equal it is not true exactly - I know you will doubt this but it is true'.[26]

A contemporary commented: *'In the firm and self-reliant tone of this passage may be seen the young man of twenty-one conscious of his power to lead others'.*[26] Wishing to create a precision machine for fast passenger trains by combining the crosshead and slide bar with outside rods connecting the wheels, Robert tried his utmost to persuade his father

'Locomotion' as modified with added blast and change of wheel design.

The No. 1 Engine on display at Darlington

against the retrograde step of adopting parallel motion offering excessive tolerances, by artfully citing the current practices of others. Thinking in terms of slow goods traffic, George did not relent, whereas Robert was prepared to push manufacturing possibilities beyond their current limits.

Working one against the other was bad for morale and therefore bad for business. In order to operate effectively, Robert wished to lead his workforce and implement his progressive design ideas without interference. The innovator reacted strongly against being meddled with. Indeed, as a necessary diversion to avoid a stalemate, it is possible that Thomas Richardson offered George Stephenson an enticing proposition to recommence working gold and silver mines in Spanish America. In the event, his brother Robert was given the task of organising the expedition and accompanying the steam engines. George received a curt note: *'I think it a good offer for thy Brother... not one day must be lost in getting forward with the Plans & I think it will be best for thee to come up with them thou' Robt. may be from home'.*[27]

The managing partner of RS&Co. needed space to contemplate his plight: a trip to the southwest of England with his uncle would help. Their purpose was to gather information about Cornish mining practices for the Spanish-American trip. Returning via London, young Robert wrote a heartfelt letter to his father from Okehampton, Devonshire on 5 March 1824:

'As far as I have proceeded on my journey to the Cornish mines, I have every reason to think it will not be misspent time; for when one is travelling about, something new generally presents itself... it seldom fails to open a new channel of ideas, which may not unfrequently prove advantageous in the end. This I think is one of the chief benefits of leaving the fireside where the young imagination received its first impression'.[26]

Unknown to Thomas Richardson, the elder Stephenson needed his feet firmly on terra firma, even though he was the obvious choice to select the workforce and order the engines. Numerous railway projects in the pipeline would soon become official, as William James's situation was deteriorating and he had been rejected by the Liverpool to Manchester railway promoters as their engineer. An influential director Joseph Sandars called a meeting of fellow shareholders to replace James because of his absence and illness. Even so, Robert Stephenson attempted to reassure his mentor: *'That line is the finest project in England'.*[24]

By 25 May 1824 Sandars could officially inform James: *'I think it right to inform you that the committee had engaged your friend G. Stephenson... The subscription list for £300,000 is filled'.*[28] George Stephenson's fund-raising abilities were second to none. He imbued shareholders with confidence concerning lucrative investments: such was the persuasive power of his personality. A friend wrote to a would-be railway shareholder on the elder Stephenson's behalf... *'how much he should feel pleased if you would ask him about these things for certainly through one means or another he gets to know the truth about speculations'.*[29] In the absence of an organised national capital market, George Stephenson played a unique part in railway investment. A link with him was a certain means by which capital could be solicited outside the investor's own area, hence his success, particularly in a buoyant market. And 1824 was a boom year.

But two of George's close relatives clearly did not approve of the repercussions which resulted from these tactics. Robert senior was to decline the Spanish American mining post and wrote to William James asking for employment on the Stratford & Moreton Railway, in order to give the unfortunate engineer much-needed support. Writing from Forth Street on 18 April 1824 he explains that although having been *'in treaty'* with the Mexican mining company he had turned the offer down. Help also came from the experienced and highly regarded engineer John Rastrick. Being fully aware of William James' predicament, Robert junior found himself in the unenviable position of knowing that his father's ambition was being realised on the back of James' misfortune. James' daughter recognised:

'Robert Stephenson experienced a severe struggle between his sense of gratitude and justice to William James, and the duty and affection which prevented his interfering with or exposing his father's pretensions: his heart was honest, while his tongue was mute'.[30]

A lack of job satisfaction and a moral dilemma made him determined to leave the railway scene for a time and let fate take its course. Robert's investigations during the visit to Cornwall and the subsequent report pleased Herring, Graham & Powles, the company behind the silver mine project and the young engineer was given charge of the expedition to Colombia. Undoubtedly behind this proposal, Thomas Richardson probably also introduced Robert to his future bride, Frances Sanderson. The Sandersons lived in Broad Street and her father was a City merchant. Robert exclaimed in a letter to Michael Longridge: *'What a place London is for prospects'.*[31]

Having done the *'setting out, the levelling and making section of Hagger Leazes Branch Railway'*,[32] Robert then spent the rest of March and early April 1824 steering the third Stockton & Darlington Railway Bill through Parliament. As the official engineer, George Stephenson was expected to attend the final stage. He procrastinated, giving the excuse to the company's lawyer on 8 April 1824: *'I am hemmed in with so much business and I am not in a state of health for such a journey'.*[33] In the event George did go, and both Stephensons submitted expenses.

Although at least two RS&Co. partners agreed with Robert's need for a break, the elder Stephenson still had to be persuaded.

Writing to Michael Longridge on 9 March from the Imperial Hotel, Covent Garden, the young engineer emphasised:

'For heaven's sake don't mention this to my father. Joseph Pease will perhaps give him the information: it will, I know, make him extremely dissatisfied, but you know I cannot by any means avoid it… Mr Powles is the head of the concern and he assures me there is no one to meddle with us. We are to have all the machinery to make, and we are to construct the road in the most advisable way we may think, after making surveys and levellings'.[31]

Thoughts of not having his son at hand to take responsibility for the necessary preliminary engineering work on all James' projected lines, caused George to resist his son's decision. There was a distinct possibility of losing Robert entirely to more amenable circumstances. Well versed in the art of persuading a predictable father, Robert began with a letter:

'But now let me beg you not to say anything against my going out to America, for I have already ordered so many instruments that it would make me look extremely foolish to call off …And only consider what an opening it is for me as an entry into business; and I am informed by all who have been there that it is a very healthy country. I must close this letter, expressing my hope that you will not go against me for this time'.[34]

On two counts of health and business, Robert could attempt to pull the strings of emotion and reason. The elder Stephenson's great fear was to lose his only son after the early death of his first wife: an anxiety that culminated in hypochondria. In 1824 it suited Robert to use a hypothetical lung condition as an excuse. In the event, the climate in Colombia would not prove conducive to his health. From the onset of his education, his father's main aim had been to make him a perfect businessman; therefore a 'business' notion would appeal to George. But in reality, the post's brief was within

Robert's experience as a mining engineer, nor can ambition or financial gain enter into the argument. The expedition's outcome was unquantifiable, with a high-risk tag. Having just met the love of his life, a selfish instinct would be to stay. And the prodigy's commitment to RS&Co. remained staunch. He directed Messrs Herring, Graham & Powles to pay £300 per annum to his father for the *'works'*.[35] To give away three-fifths of his salary was a measure of his responsibility.

Returning to Newcastle from London at the beginning of April, 'he could not settle down... friends were anxious for him'.[36] Robert Stephenson was suffering from depression. Contemporaries recognised: *'After two years of laborious application to the study and practice of his profession, his failing health give evidence of overwork'*.[37] Dr Headlam strongly urged a long sea voyage for an inevitable rest of at least five weeks. In no way can Robert Stephenson be described as *'dilatory'*,[38] just the opposite. Too much had been and was expected of him. *'Sorely against his will George give his consent'*.[34]

In the line of duty, the young engineer then trained four of the RS&Co. workforce, including Locke, to survey and execute plans and sections in order to serve his father's ambition. Later, Robert boasted how he could *'make an ordinary man understand levelling in a day'*.[39] Also it had been expected that George Stephenson would furnish the *'Plans which may be required'*[40] for RS&Co. But the lot fell to his diligent son. Robert executed plans of stationary engines enabling orders to be carried out in his absence. Other plans for the Stockton & Darlington Railway almost certainly included the intended iron bridge across the river Skerne, and the design of an anticipated locomotive order, which was a compromise on the firmly held ideas of the two Stephensons. Nicholas Wood stated how Robert assisted his father during the railway's construction: *'in the surveys and levelling... and*

in the drawing and construction of the locomotive engines'.[41] It would appear that the castings may well have been done for *Active*, renamed *Locomotion*, and her sisters; indeed Robert did not see the need for a replacement working manager outside the RS&Co. workforce. In the limited time available, he even sent *'plans'*[42] to Newcastle before he set sail.

Back in London, Robert prepared for the expedition and would be pleased to increase his knowledge of chemistry. He thoroughly read *'all the requisite practical information'*,[43] taking lessons from Richard Phillips, the Professor of Mineralogical Chemistry, as well as learning Spanish. The emotionally frustrated youth wrote to his stepmother on 4 June: *'This week in London has been one of the most miserable ones I have ever had in my short experience'*.[42] He goes on to say that he would be glad to help on *'the undertaking at Liverpool but I do not even now despair of taking the chief part of his [father's] engagements on myself in a year or two'*.[42]

Gaining in confidence with every day spent in the company of scientific academics and City business magnates, Robert wrote with conviction: *'I have the satisfaction to say that I never in my whole life spent so much time to so much advantage as I have done since I left home....all is meant right'*.[42] With his friend Charles Empsom, who was to act as a secretary, he packed up and mounted the coach for Falmouth only to be given instructions to unload and start for Liverpool instead, which was opportune in that he could see his father again. The journey would focus his thoughts that promoting a comfortable means of transport as an alternative network for passengers ought not to be difficult:

'I never recollect in all my travels being so terrified on a coach. I expected every moment for many miles that we should be upset, and if such an accident had happened, we must have

literally been crushed to pieces ... the coach top on which we came was actually rent; all the springs, when we arrived at Liverpool, was destitute of any elasticity, one of them absolutely broken and the body of the coach resting on the framework, so that, in fact, we rattled into this town more like a stage wagon than a light coach'.[44]

The last epistle in this exciting epoch of Robert Stephenson's eventful life was written by George Stephenson to Michael Longridge on 15 June 1824. It serves as evidence of the affection between father and son.

'It gave me great pleasure to see Robert again... There is a Doctor Trail, a clever mineralogist and some famous mathematicians that we have dined with. I was much satisfied to find that Robert could acquit himself so well among them. He was much improved in expressing himself since I had last seen him; the poor fellow is in good spirits about going abroad and I must make the most of it'.[44]

Three days later Robert embarked on a voyage with little to do. At night his ceiling was a mass of stars. On board the *Sir William Congreve* he could contemplate a rocket, a revolution in communication.

THE AMERICAS: 1824 - 1827

After disembarking at La Guayra, Colombia on 23 July 1824, Robert Stephenson reassessed his preconceptions about the terrain. Concerning the intended eight mile railway to Caracas, he wrote of the precipitous ascents and descents; of a country *'thickly set with hills, several thousand feet high'*.[1] His report ends: *'I think it would not be prudent... to commence the speculation'*.[1] Later machinery had to be abandoned on the shore, orders for stationary engines cancelled.

On reaching the vicinity of Mariquita Robert adapted to the job in hand, reopening mines and making them profitable for the Colombian Mining Association. *'He explored the country... made assays of specimens of ore; wrote reams of letters and reports many of which ...have* *considerable literary merits; drew out a sketch for an efficient administration of mines and in every way strove to earn and save money for the association'*.[2]

For three years he enjoyed the magnificent scenery, the challenge of using chemical analysis to determine the most economical way to extract metal from ores and ensuring the continuation of his education. South America was a finishing school. Nicholas Wood recalled his former pupil's distinctive characteristics: *'profound thought; intense and severe study and application; great natural genius and indomitable perseverance'*.[3] To his house in Santa Ana, built of flattened bamboo, smooth reeds and palm leaves:

Robert's house at Santa Ana, Colombia

'…visitors came from Bogotá and Mariquita, and for weeks together he had with him M. Boussingault and Dr Roullin. The former was an accomplished chemist and geologist; the latter had been invited to become Professor of Mathematics…Under their guidance Robert Stephenson studied with system and accuracy the higher branches of mathematics and various departments of natural science'.[4]

When the scientific worth of his friend and teacher M. Boussingault was disparaged by the mining company's secretary in London, Robert came to his defence:

'Practical men are certainly to be esteemed as such, but I am far from attaching the importance to them which our masters appear inclined to do. Indeed, in the working of gold and silver mines in veins in this country, it is absolutely essential that theory and practice should be united and go hand in hand; not that the former should be appreciated beyond its value, and the other depreciated below it, but that both should be entitled to equal consideration and weight'.[5]

By applying this philosophy also to locomotives and railway construction, he succeeded where other pioneers had failed. Self-imposed systematic scientific and mathematical study gave him essential knowledge. Thoroughly well versed in what was then called mineralogical chemistry, combustion and alloys, he could pursue his career as a railway engineer with confidence.

'It was not until the end of October 1825, that miners had been collected in sufficient numbers to commence operations'.[6] Therefore he divided his time between 'eating and studying'.[7] The laboratory was his haven, 'where I make my chemical experiments which stink with all sorts of gases - Bottles and Glass jars stand all around just like a Doctor's shop'.[8] Robert ends his letter of 28 April 1825 to his stepmother with the request: 'Pray do let Thomas Nicholson and Joseph Locke write regularly to me - let me hear everything about home, the factory etc etc it relieves me vastly'.[8]

Initially, Robert had taken ore samples to test and find out how much silver was present in order to decide which mines were worth re-opening; then he recovered silver from low grade mine waste. Being an essential part of the extraction process, Robert Stephenson's ability to do this work well ensured productivity and greater profits for the owners.

Given another environment between 1803 and 1824 he might have preferred the life of an academic with the occasional challenge of discussions with like minds. Robert wrote a letter of appreciation to the Columbian Mining Association's agent R.S.Illingworth: 'My residence in this country, and the work I have had to perform, would have been irksome in the extreme, had I not been fortunate in meeting you'.[9] He goes on to explain how 'the art of mining'[9] gave him much pleasure:

'but I should wish to blend other studies with it… should I remain here, and would erect a complete laboratory for performing all the necessary kinds of metallurgical operations. I would have a liberal supply of scientific journals as well as standard works on chemistry and mineralogy. Those…would form ample resources for the mind'.[9]

What was he doing in a mundane administrative job ensuring money for someone else's company through efficient administration and scientific methodology, when the factory, established with Robert's interests in mind and offering state-of-the-art technology, was going to the wall due to his absence? In this heartfelt letter written to Illingworth on 24 March 1825, he divulged: 'What I might do in England is, perhaps, known to myself only'.[9]

Messages from abroad caused him constant anxiety. Michael Longridge wrote: 'Robert! my faith in engineers is wonderfully shaken. I hope when you return to us your accuracy will redeem their character'.[10] Sometimes the reality of failure was carefully camouflaged in a profusion of poetic expression, as in the letters of Joseph Locke. Others were blunt. On 9 April 1827 Edward Pease wrote to his young protégé:

'I can assure thee that thy business at Newcastle, as well as thy father's engineering, have suffered very much from thy absence and unless thou soon return, the former will be given up… What is done is not done with credit to the house'.[11]

Left to carry out his own locomotive design intentions and methods of railway construction, George Stephenson was exposed as being incorrect; his sincerely held 'economics' were in fact false economies. Only now did Pease realise that he had been backing the wrong Stephenson. Initially, the immediate impression of George's intuitive flair had won the day. Great Britain was enjoying an economic boom. Riding high on the crest of an ambitious wave, the elder Stephenson persuaded his RS&Co. partners to found a new company, George Stephenson & Son, on 31 December 1824 in order to implement his grandiose railway schemes. Robert was named as principal engineer, sharing a salary with George but significantly, given the option of resigning on his return. The new firm occupied an office next to that of RS&Co., the intention being to provide an integrated service for prospective railway companies from surveying to completion.

Promotion of George's image formed a fundamental part of his partners' objectives. Edward Pease wrote to Thomas Richardson: *'I have pressed on GS - he should always be a gentleman in his dress, his clothes neat & new, & of the best quality, all his personal linen clean every day. His hat & upper coat conspicuously good, without dandyism… Thy affect. Cousin'.*[12]

Alarmed by the anticipated work of Nicholas Wood about the history of railway technology, Michael Longridge wrote to Edward Pease on 18 January 1825: *'Wood's Book must undergo a strict censorship before it is published - and I fear this will be a work of considerable delicacy, but it must be done'.*[13] So Pease had the task of persuading the author to promote George Stephenson's locomotive development plans,

as opposed to those of his son. Wood replied to Pease that if publishing *'should injure Mr. Stephenson I should notwithstanding withhold them, but after mature consideration I do not think they will - they are only conveying information which every man in a short time will have an opportunity of informing himself'…*[14]

Consequently the author completely obliterates Robert's major locomotive contribution between 1819 & 22. Then, when George's efforts proved to be wrong, Wood was left to take the blame; whereas he only ever expressed his friend's views under pressure. And on this issue the highly respected mining engineer had to dissemble in all his future publications on behalf of his revered business partner. He later bitterly retorted; *'I have felt those remarks very keenly as being very unjust and unmerited'*[15] and goes on to stress how he was only reiterating the elder Stephenson's *'own recommendations'*[15] in 1825 and how his views on locomotives were in fact *'extremely limited'*[15] at this time.

George Stephenson was always right! Whereas Robert wished to alter and improve *'this that and the other detail of the machine, his father defended the existing arrangements'*[16]. The pivoted axle was a feature of the first few Stockton & Darlington Railway locomotives, as was the outside rod coupling the wheels, yet in 1825 Wood sang the praises of George's steam springs and continued to promote the continuous chain. As soon as Robert left for South America, the blast action was removed from the Stephenson locomotives due to an apparent *'rapid consumption of fuel'.*[17] Removing it was, as Nicholas Wood put it… *'a means of economising the fuel… the engine might then be made to assume the character of a low-pressure engine'.*[17] Wood explained, *'by enlarging the flue tube and giving it a double turn through the boiler we have got a sufficiency of steam without it'.*[17]

The blast action was absent from all Stockton & Darlington Railway locomotives constructed at RS&Co. between 1825-7 and at least one was fitted with a return flue. Visiting this railway in 1827, two Prussian engineers noted how: *'another boiler serving for a similar locomotive had a return flue…which enters into the chimney at the end where the fire takes place…the exhaust steam being discharged without further ado into the atmosphere'.*[18]

One letter in particular would give Robert Stephenson an impetus to return. On 23 February 1827, George wrote to his absent son concerning the L&MR. Feeling sorry for himself, he wrote of being *'greatly disapointed at you not geting home as soon as was expected… I must waddle on as well as I can until you get to joine me'.*[19] And then continues in his own handwriting:

'…The estimate for this concern is 500000£ and I daresay it will require it all the line passes Rainhill very near the same place where Jameses line passed we shall want one steam engine at that place and a nother at near parr moss… I want these engines to be constantly moveing with an endless Rope so that the locomotive engines can take hold of the Rope and go on with out stoping. The Incline plane will only be 3/8 of an inch per yard [1 in 96] so that the poor [power] of the locomotive assisted by the perment ones will get the traffict on in grand stile. we most go at 10 miles per hour I think I told you about my

George Stephenson's 'Experiment' 1827 from John Rastrick's notebook, January 1829

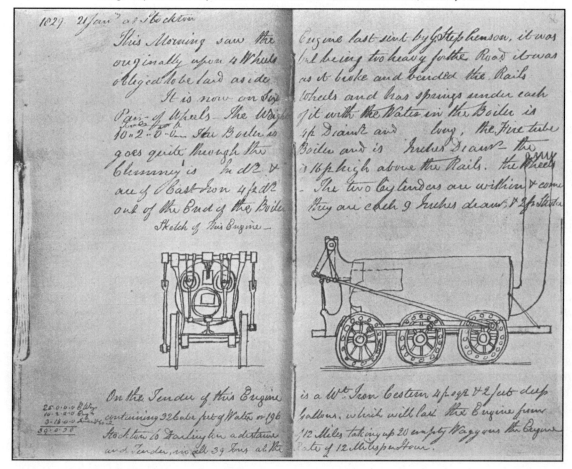

new plan of locomotive it will be a huge job the Cylinder is intirly within the Bolior... and I will not use more than the coals that has heather to been used you will think I have some mistaken ideas about this but I think not - and you may depend upon it that if you do not get home soon everything will be at prefecttion and then there will be nothing for you to do or invent - however we will hope that some usefull Ideas will be brought from the western world'.[19]

With all the known disruptions caused by a mixture of motive powers, Robert's dismay at his father's continuing advocacy of inclines placed centrally on what was intended to be a fast track for passengers, can be imagined. Also George's *'huge job'* in order to increase the locomotives heating surface, would be unwelcome news when the rails at the time could not withstand extra weight. In contrast, Robert aimed to produce a rapid generation of · steam by increasing the amount of tubes in the boiler, enabling a light simple design capable of mounting inclines and travelling at speed.

A multi-water-tube boiler patent had been taken out by Trevithick just before he set sail for South America in 1815. The young locomotive enthusiast Robert Stephenson was also aware of extremely advanced engines being used in the USA over a long period; John Stevens had introduced a multi-fire-tube boiler in his steam-powered boats. Consequently, Robert wrote to Michael Longridge:

'We have now got a steam-boat in action on the river Magdalena... The engines are from the United States, where I have heard they have the finest steam-boats in the world; and as the communication from Carthagena to that country is frequent, I have some intention of seeing their steam machinery. It is the best way home, a regular packet being established between New York and Liverpool'.[20]

Did the voyager determine to meet both Trevithick and Stevens en route to England? An eyewitness was adamant that Robert's rendezvous with Richard Trevithick was planned and not an *'accident'.*[21] Circumstantial evidence suggests this statement to be correct, but typically Robert would later wish to convey a different impression.

Little had been heard of the inventor since his departure for Peru on 20 October 1816. Likewise persuaded as to the possibilities of restoring silver mines at Pasco to their former high level of production by the introduction of steam engines, for the previous five years Trevithick had been designing engines and exporting them. *'Several engines and plunger pumps were made, no piece to be larger than a mule could carry'.*[22] One invoice described *'chimney, axles, carriage wheels etc,'*[22] possibly with a view to *'steam locomotion in the Cordilleras'.*[22] Certainly the designer mentions a named engine in a letter to Rastrick's factory on 4 September 1813: *'Mr. Uville and I shall leave Cornwall for Bridgnorth on our journey to town. We are both very anxious to see the Sans Pareil at work'.*[22] Maybe one underlying reason for Robert Stephenson's decision to accept the Colombian post, was to track Trevithick down via the Mining Association. The inventor held many keys to success.

Return journey

In the middle of July, Stephenson was able to leave Santa Ana and make plans for his homeward journey via Carthegena and New York. Robert had reason to be proud of leading a successful enterprise under difficult conditions. An admiring father wrote: 'There has been a florishing a count of your men in the English pappers and great creadit is given to <u>Robert Stephenson</u> for his good management of them'. Engineering colleagues also recorded: *'he accomplished his mission with great credit and made some investigations and reports which exhibit great foresight and talent'.*[19]

Two very different men, one impulsive the other reserved, came face-to-face at an inn in Carthagena: *'There is no doubt that the discussions on the steam engine between these original geniuses... had significant consequences'.*[23] Trevithick broke the ice: *'Is that Bobby? I've nursed you many a time!'*[24] Animated talks then followed to the embarrassment of all observers: *'two of a trade cannot agree'.*[21] For Robert in particular, arguments spelt progress. By focusing on what was relevant, he sifted and then retained the information given to him.

Regarding the various forms of tubular boilers, after experimenting for a week Trevithick had designed and put *'into execution an entirely new boiler composed of numerous tubes'.*[25] His aim was always *'to avoid the loss of power by loss of heat'.*[25] His friend Davies Gilbert had advised the inventor on 31 December 1815: *'There is without doubt sufficient surface, but then a great part of the long tubes will be remote from the fire'.*[25] Commenting on the accompanying sketch in 1872, Francis Trevithick realised the similarity of *'fixing of tubes in modern locomotive fire-boxes'.*[25] Did the exchange of ideas in 1827 lead to Robert adopting the immediately adjacent firebox to his multitubular boiler two years later?

Conserving heat in a stationary engine was not a problem; clearly Trevithick also contemplated the best solution for a travelling engine. Robert Stephenson's adoption of the crank axle was suggested during one of their conversations: *'Trevithick stated there was 40 percent increase in the duty of Watt's engine (worked expansively) in Cornwall, from putting a jacket on the cylinders'.*[26] Robert later explained why he placed the locomotive cylinders in the smokebox:

'Mr Trevithick, who in the course of some experiments, had built a brick flue round the cylinder, and had applied the heat of a fire directly to the metal with very beneficial results, as regarded the economical use of steam.'[26]

As well as a compact boiler with a large heating surface in the form of tubes, there was also a need for a fundamental design change to create a fast locomotive. Robert wished to simplify the engine as Richard Trevithick had done before him. *Catch-me-who-can* of 1808 had single driving wheels, and in his steam road carriage of 1802 the inventor of the high pressure engine had also introduced large driving wheels and the concept of cylinders set horizontally to go with the motion,

'That steam locomotion should form a constant topic of conversation between two such men was only natural... and Robert Stephenson... was well inclined to listen to what was then considered the "visionary schemes" of Trevithick, whose utmost ideas of attainable speed were, however, so soon to be far exceeded'.[27]

Contemporaries recognised: *'There is no doubt that the original and daring views of Trevithick with respect to the capabilities of the locomotive made a deep impression on Robert Stephenson'.*[28]

'With a hundred pounds in his pocket, the young engineer gave fifty to Trevithick to enable him to reach England'.[29] Taking a direct route, he arrived first in early October. The rest of Trevithick's party, John Gerard and the *'two Monteleagre boys'*[30] bound for boarding school in England, then arranged to travel back via New York with Robert Stephenson, his secretary Charles Empson and a servant. Gerard, like Stephenson, was an employee of a mining *'Association'*[30] and had brought Trevithick from Costa Rica to Carthagena. Gerard wrote to the inventor in Cornwall on 17 November 1827 from London:

'I arrived here from Liverpool last night... The brig Bunker's Hill in which we came from Carthagena to New York, was wrecked within a few hours sail from the port. We were in a disagreeable situation for some time, but more afraid than hurt. The cargo was nearly all lost... The boys are well and desire their respect to you'.[31]

This shipwreck had a profound effect upon Robert Stephenson, especially an incident whereby the ship's mate ensured an obnoxious person's safety before the rest of the passengers, because they were both Freemasons and bound under an oath to help each other. With memories of his admired mentor the Grand Master William James foremost in his mind, Robert determined to join the fraternity. St Andrew's Lodge of the State of New York gave the new *'master-mason of good report, beloved and esteemed among us'*[32] a document under their seal on 21 September 1827. Robert would be dutiful within an ordered context, yet still true to his own convictions.

In the immediate aftermath of this decision Robert's generosity saved the day, and he was able to obtain enough money in New York to provide for all of them. His friends accompanied him inland to Montreal, via land and water. During this time he made contacts in the hope of securing orders for RS&Co., notably from the Stevens family and undoubtedly fulfilled his vow not only to view the steamboats but also to travel by them up the Hudson river and along Lake Ontario. At Montreal, they went to a succession of balls given by colonial dignitaries before returning to New York. This hospitality would leave Robert in high spirits for the tasks ahead. He and his companions then took a first-class packet the *Pacific* to Liverpool.

NEWCASTLE upon TYNE: 1828 - 1833

For the next five years, Newcastle was to be Robert's headquarters, *'superintending the factory and originating or developing those improvements in the structure of the locomotive which raised it to its present efficiency from its unsatisfactory state at the opening of the Stockton & Darlington Railway'*.[1] Apart from Samuel Smiles who had been misled until he had received a communication in 1857 when it was too late to retract; all contemporary commentators gave the resounding message that Robert Stephenson was the inspiration behind the prototype locomotive, the instigator of efficient production methods and the driving force encouraging his employees at Robert Stephenson & Company (RS&Co).

Immediate business occupied him in London and the continent, offering opportunities to visit Miss Fanny Sanderson of Broad Street and matters to settle but not end, with the Colombian Mining Association. Robert Stephenson kept his options open just in case. After all, his work abroad had brought him acclaim in the national newspapers, a feather in most people's cap without a visionary intent amounting to an obsession.

Robert Stephenson & Co. Locomotive construction shed in c. 1828

Locomotive design development

Returning to Liverpool, the working manager of RS&Co. wrote to Michael Longridge on 1st January 1828:

'Since I came down from London, I have been talking a great deal to my father about endeavouring to reduce the size and ugliness of our travelling engines, by applying the engine on the side of the boiler or beneath it entirely, somewhat similarly to Gurney's steam-coach'...[2]

Unfortunately he was held back from implementing Trevithick's suggestion of placing the cylinders beneath the boiler in order to conserve heat, a practice already adopted by the inventor's successors on steam road carriages operating regularly in London, until eventual competition within the railway industry forced a decision and gave Robert an opportunity to cement his ideas. He probably had opposition from others with an aversion to crank axles, as well as from his own father. But after years of unsuccessful persuasion, Robert was at last allowed to simplify locomotive design. George finally abandoned the 'nostrum' of indirect drive, his last effort, the *Experiment* of 1827 earning the nickname 'Old Elbows'.

Hoping for automatic orders from the Liverpool & Manchester Railway (L&MR), which

Robert Stephenson's Lancashire Witch January 1828 intended for L & MR transferred to B&LR August 1828

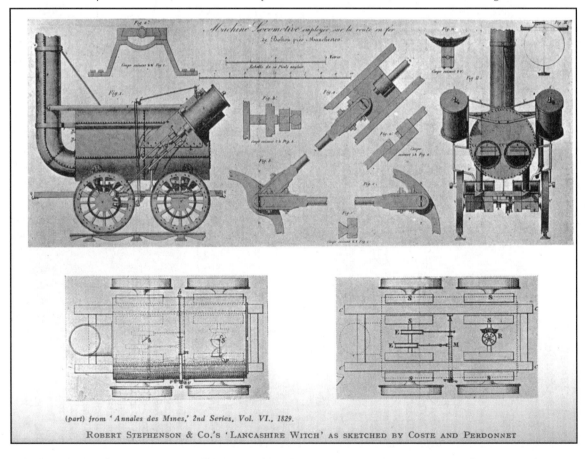

(part) from 'Annales des Mines,' 2nd Series, Vol. VI., 1829.

ROBERT STEPHENSON & CO.'S 'LANCASHIRE WITCH' AS SKETCHED BY COSTE AND PERDONNET

was envisaged as the core of a national passenger network, Robert Stephenson instigated his locomotive development programme on returning to Newcastle. With clear objectives in mind and the aim for speed, economy, comfort and reliability, two locomotives could be built for each new link in the chain. In this way there would be no costly mistakes. It is fortunate that two French engineers, Coste and Perdonnet, wrote a detailed description in 1828 of his first experiment intended to *'serve as a model'*[3] for the L&MR locomotives. As mainstream components, Robert introduced direct drive from external cylinders to the axles in combination with the outside rods connecting the wheels, steel leaf springs and the blast pipe to stimulate the fire. For the first time, Robert also obtained the expansive working of steam. Undoubtedly this had been a topic of conversation with Richard Trevithick in Cartegena.

Until the quality of iron proved to be sufficiently reliable, Robert Stephenson was prepared to go backwards by returning to Iron Age chariot wheel technology. The Losh / Stephenson 1816 locomotive serving the Kilmarnock & Troon railway had almost certainly been modified while Robert was in Edinburgh, either on Stockton & Darlington business or while at university: *'the iron wheels of this engine were afterwards removed and replaced with wooden wheels when it was again placed upon the road and continued working until the year 1848'.*[4] During Robert's absence, Nicholas Wood continued this practice and he was 'in complete agreement with Mr Stephenson as to their superiority'[3] over cast iron wheels at this time. Broken wheels resulted in disruption; delays would soon deter even the most enthusiastic railway traveller. It was noted at Killingworth that whereas cast iron wheels soon became worn and friction *'considerably increased',*[3] wooden wheels with wrought iron tyres were *'not visibly affected'.*[3]

Also *'steel leaf springs'*[5] had been introduced on heavy royal state coaches during the previous century but were expensive, almost certainly the reason why elder Stephenson rejected what was technically possible in 1816 and resorted to his ingenious, but impractical steam springs. Coste and Perdonnet recognised the locomotive from the workshops of Mr Robert Stephenson of Newcastle as *'the most perfect yet constructed'.*[3] They specifically noted particulars that distinguish this locomotive from others which they had viewed in the region:

'It is carried on springs while the other engines are not so carried, or only as we have just explained. [i.e. by the steam springs of Losh and Stephenson]'.[3]

Evidently Nicholas Wood did not give instructions to introduce steel leaf springs on the Killingworth and Hetton locomotives until well after Robert's return from South America in November 1827. Indeed Wood had remained entirely loyal to the elder Stephenson's mistaken policies, even though between 1819-21, the mining engineer had given his apprentice essential help to improve the locomotive's efficient working. This is significant: the instigator Robert Stephenson continued the work.

By 1821, the valve driving gear could be operated by hand, as is evident from contemporary drawings. Six years later, two Prussian engineers gave a written account of the Killingworth practice prevailing on the Stockton & Darlington Railway's locomotives:

'... in order to make the engine go backwards and forwards the eccentrics, or rather the hooks by which they are moved, stand on the shaft at a right angle. From each eccentric leads the driving rod, which can be put in and out of gear with the lever arms which move the valve. This method of reversing the piston stroke is the simplest and renders unnecessary many valve rods, which were formerly required in the application of the eccentric. With this arrangement the change of direction of going can be undertaken with one cylinder, the other helping to come in, in order to bring the crank pins under the dead points'.[6]

For the driver to be able to engage and

disengage in this way was significant. Improvements to the driving gear or as Robert termed it *'working gear'*,[6] remained a major consideration to the young factory Chief until the ultimate 'link motion' was achieved.

Engineer-in-Chief to railway companies

Throughout his life in pursuit of perfection, Robert Stephenson pushed manufacturing beyond the limits. One of his first tasks in 1828 was to instruct an apprentice, John Cass Birkinshaw, *'to make a series of sketches of all machinery in vogue'*[7] including furnaces, rolling mills and forges at Bedlington Iron Works for his use. Under Robert's auspices, wrought iron became the predominant metal for weight bearing spans in the railway industry: railway lines, station roofs, locomotive frames and bridges to cross roads, canals and the sea. Allowing complete clearance for restrictions imposed by navigation authorities, the metal beam became fundamentally important. Robert Stephenson explained how iron was:

'...an absolute necessity in Railway Bridge construction where headway is so frequently of paramount importance, and where a rapidity of execution is often a more necessary consideration than even economy or durability; while defective foundations that have so often to be contended with, render the lightness, the independent strength, and pliable character of iron for such structure of the utmost value'.[8]

Out of duty, Robert Stephenson did not take the option of leaving George Stephenson & Son (GS&Son), but in remaining faithful to his senior partners, neither would he sacrifice his own intentions. In order to put his concepts at the disposal of progress, Robert was prepared to mix with the *'enemy'*, that is competitors: indeed he endeared himself to engineers such as John Rastrick and George Leather.

It suited Robert to be Engineer-in-Chief of railways both for those primarily intended for passengers and also those serving collieries. In this way he could test his locomotives during the construction process, thus becoming aware of running problems, but hopefully gaining orders for RS&Co. once the railways were operational. And it suited him to take over the almost complete Canterbury & Whitstable Railway, previously engineered by Joseph Locke and John Dixon. He wrote to a friend in March 1828: *'If I may judge from appearances I am to get the Canterbury Railway, which you know is no inconvenient distance from London... all my arrangement instinctively regarded Broad Street as the pole?'*[9] This was the street where his bride-to-be lived.

Safeguarding his investment in RS&Co and GS&Son, Thomas Richardson sought to question how the *'giddy lover'*[10] could take on so much at once. In customary manner, Robert wrote a courteous reply as to how he intended to operate as Engineer-in-Chief to numerous railway companies:

'They would not expect my whole time to be devoted to it, as an assistant to be always attending would be requisite; so that it would not require me to confine my attention to that neighbourhood entirely.

I should then have the Lancashire and the Warrington & Newton to attend to. Amongst them I should divide my attention, and I see no difficulty in doing that, when I have a confidential assistant at each place to see that my plans are carefully and strictly attended to...'[11]

The greater the preliminary planning and detailed designs, the more he could delegate with confidence until he had trained teams of engineers as extensions of himself. Only then would he be able to allow degrees of initiative. However, Robert's immediate concern as joint chief engineer to the company George Stephenson & Son was a lack of credibility.

The Liverpool & Manchester Railway

On the face of it, sections had progressed well in the experienced hands of the contractor John Stephenson and his workforce. The 2000 yard long Wapping Tunnel, the massive Olive Mount cutting and the Broad Green embankment were of an unprecedented scale. Robert wrote to Michael Longridge on 1 January 1828: *'I have just returned from a ride along the line for seven miles, in which distance I have not been a little surprised to find excavations of such magnitude'*.[2]

Deriving the methodology from Robert Stannard, agent of his friend William Roscoe, Joseph Locke had initiated the correct solution to traverse Chat Moss. He then replaced Charles Vignoles on the western half of the line as George's only *'Assistant Engineer'*.[12] And there was an official glowing recognition; *'On his return in 1828, Robert Stephenson found that great work far towards completion, under the unconquerable energies of his father, and his earnest and able assistant, Mr Joseph Locke'*.[13]

But a very bitter Vignoles had complained, *'the mode Mr Stephenson proposes to put the works into the course of operation is not the most eligible'*[14]. If possible, Robert must prevent his father from implementing piecemeal methods again, whereby *'at the onset of the undertaking he had only a general notion of the labour before him. The details were not considered till their consideration could no longer be deferred... each day to care of its own evils'*.[15] This made conditions very difficult for those working under him. Extra planning, reports and problem spans, such as oblique bridges, could be done at Newcastle, where Robert in fact spent most of his time. It has been stressed that railway *'undertakings were trifles'* and made little impact on his time and creative energy. Even so his essential work on this railway was recognised: *'Whilst engaged after his arrival in England, in assisting his father in the construction of the Liverpool and Manchester Railway, Robert Stephenson at this time directed his attention to the systems of railway traction...'*[16]

The future of Robert Stephenson & Company

'The great and immediate work for Robert Stephenson ... was to raise the efficiency of the locomotive so that on the completion of the Liverpool & Manchester line, it should be adopted by the directors as the main power of their railway'.[17] The fate of his factory was of paramount importance to him. From the outset he had realised that only by having specialist employees, combined with an insistence on *'accuracy'*[18] could the perfect action of engines be achieved. During his absence these ideals had gone to the wall. Instead of investing in a committed workforce, a defeatist attitude prevailed such as *'laying off hands'*. Since the summer of 1826 William Hutchinson had been left to fend for himself and complaints about the early locomotives abounded from Timothy Hackworth, the Stockton & Darlington Railway Company engine superintendent. Trained labour in particular fields of engineering was expensive.

Precision workmanship was also costly. Yet, certain of his convictions, Robert returned and built up a team of technicians, not only to serve the factory, but the railway world for a generation. *'Many of the eminent railway engineers of the 19th-century had been apprenticed to Robert Stephenson & Co... no one man among them combined so remarkable a degree the long experience and practical qualities of Robert Stephenson himself.'*[19]

Maintaining standards despite the expense, Robert defended his stance and wrote to Thomas Richardson: *'we cannot really compete with those engine-builders in the neighbourhood of Newcastle, who not only work for nothing, but who make bad workmanship... I know it is impossible to make a good and substantial job without reasonable prices'.*[20]

Boiler development

George Stephenson boasted to his son on 31 January 1828: *'With respect to the engine for Liverpool… recollect what a number we shall want - I should think thirty'.*[21] Unfortunately Robert was unable to instigate an immediate development programme and his progressive ideas were cocooned for almost eighteen months. Having had a business agreement with the Jameses involving a multi-water-tube boiler, George Stephenson could be open to accusations of plagiarism in this field, but he *'had the great advantage of close personal intimacy with Mr Booth, the treasurer of the Liverpool and Manchester Railway'*[22] (L&MR). Henry Booth had not seen WH James's boiler.

On 30 April 1827 his Company allowed him *'£100 to make any experiments'*[21] to develop an effective boiler capable of using coke. Having received the funding and with a fondness for mechanics, Booth insisted that his ideas were put into practice. Consequently on 7 January 1828, the elder Stephenson told the Board of a *'new construction, the result of experiments by himself and the Treasurer'.*[21] From the ensuing letters, it is possible to say that Robert was under pressure from the L&MR engineer and treasurer to adopt first of all a water-filled tubular boiler, and then another whim of Booth's concerning two boilers with separate chimneys, against his better judgment. After all Robert had been pursuing a multi-fire-tube boiler first in the USA, then in France, as the way forward but he did not get this chance until April

1829. The sketch for their first boiler suggestion 'with small tubes that contained the water' was sent from Liverpool by George Stephenson to his son on 8 January 1828 with an added postscript *'the small tubes will not require to be so strong as other parts of the boiler',*[21] ending in typical panache *'you must calculate that this engine will be for all the engineers in the Kingdom - nay, indeed, the world - to look at'.*[21] A few weeks later George wrote again to Robert, *'With respect to the engine for Liverpool… Mr Booth and myself think two chimneys would be better than one, say eight inches in diameter and not to exceed fifteen feet'.*[21]

Clearly from George Stephenson's reactions, Robert objected to the complexity of Booth's multi-water-tube boiler, only to be reminded that the bent tube aspect was his idea, so get on with the job. On the 15 April 1828, the latter received a letter from his father: *'I am quite aware that the bent tubes are a complicated job to make, but… This bent tube is a child of your own… The*

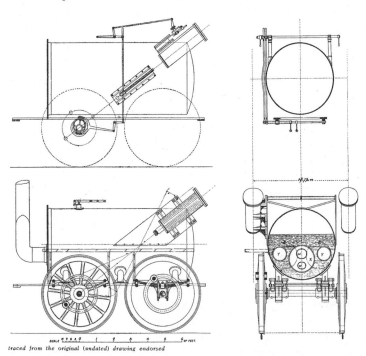

scale ... 1 ... 2 ... 3 ... 4 ... 5 OF FEET

traced from the original (undated) drawing endorsed

'Liverpool', January 1828 with multi tube boiler as proposed by Henry Booth

interior of a watch looks complicated, but when once lit up, there needs very little trouble for one hundred years'...[21] Five days later George again argued his case for a means of cleaning out the fire deposits from their proposed boiler: '... This nozzle piece would easily be taken out at any time and the fire cleaned at the hole. This I think may be done while the engine is working upon an easy part of the road'.[21] That the elder Stephenson was not a speed enthusiast is not only evident from contemporary statements but also his proposals: in this case cleaning out the locomotive while operating. He also suggests the compromise... 'It appears to me it will be found better to feed one time with coke and the next with coal. I think the one would revive the other'.[21] And the L&MR was legally bound to a clean air policy.

This boiler was a disaster. Robert's knowledge of chemistry would have forewarned him of the consequences concerning the use of impure water - 'the tubes became furred with deposits and burned-out'.[23] Both locomotives sent to the continent had also been fitted with these small water tubes; even more reason then for a multi-tubular boiler filled with the fire gases.

In the meantime Robert modified the 'Liverpool Travelling Engine' to two single flues, thus doubling the heating surface without the design disadvantage of a return flue which entailed the driver and fire man being at opposite ends of the locomotive: another distinct disadvantage if anticipating travelling at speed. Renamed the *Lancashire Witch* at the opening of the Bolton & Leigh Railway on 1 August 1828, the *Liverpool Mercury* recorded:

'The engine employed on this occasion was originally constructed for the Liverpool and Manchester railroad, by Mr Robert Stephenson, the son of the engineer of that magnificent undertaking. It is of eight horse-power, and is calculated to convey a load of twenty tons, at the rate of seven miles an hour. To economise the fuel, an apparatus had been attached to the engine for working the steam expansively, which fully answers the expectation of the makers: the advantage gained by this modification of high-pressured steam, has been sufficiently proved in fixed engines, by various engineers, but this is the first locomotive to which it has been applied'.[24]

The innovator's disappointment can be imagined when this very significant locomotive was transferred to a minor railway. Booth's boiler development contribution now terminated.

Locomotives versus stationary engines

With continuing locomotive design uncertainty arising from the Booth / elder Stephenson intervention, a deputation of directors including Henry Booth, was asked to report on the Stockton & Darlington Railway. Time was short. Robert appealed to those in the new railway industry to support the locomotive. To Longridge he wrote: 'I am much pleased that you are interesting yourself in the suit of Locomotive versus Stationary. It is a subject worthy of your aid and best wishes; but you must bear in mind best wishes alone won't do'.[25] And also to Timothy Hackworth:

'Please write by return of post, or at all events at your earliest convenience, answer to these queries. I cannot wonder at the travelling engine having so much to contend with, when I come in contact with enemies to them every hour; and they prove to be enemies without reason'.[26]

At the same time, his father also wrote to Hackworth, admitting that his opinion of locomotives had deteriorated; indeed, he was promoting his design of a horse-driven 'Dandy' cart as a serious motive power proposition, and explained '...but I never considered it ought to be tried at Darlington as I then considered the locomotive a better thing'.[27]

L&MR directors Booth, Moss and Cropper were instructed to take into account first of all the cost, and then wear and tear, both to the engines and the road. Damage done to the excessive weight of the locomotive appears to have been a major concern and there was a distinct possibility of employing Benjamin Thomson's system of stationary engines throughout, as on the Brunton and Shields Railway. But Cropper was not so much anti-locomotive as part of a very strong anti-Stephenson lobby that existed within the L&MR Board, partly due to the elder Stephenson's monopoly tactics and partly to past loyalties. William James's persuasion as to the business advantages of fast communication had not fallen on stony ground. Whatever the motive power chosen, it had to be worthy of a high investment and the Directors' expectation of speed and reliability.

A resulting *'inconclusive'*[28] report written by Henry Booth, evoked a lengthy reply dated 5 November 1828, signed by George but written in Robert Stephenson's hand and style of expression: *'This data is far from being applicable to the Liverpool & Manchester Road'.*[29] The next day a debate among the L&MR Directors took place leading to the authorisation of yet another deputation, and the engineers John Rastrick and James Walker were appointed.

This time the locomotive enthusiasts Robert Stephenson and Joseph Locke were present when these two senior engineers visited railways in the North-east, in the hope of influencing them; pointing out this and that and giving them relevant information. During the next six months, both young men became effective politicians. Unlike most of the L&MR board of directors whose major priority was for a fast track between the two major business centres, Robert and Joseph wanted a flexible power system for a national railway network.

The RS&Co. managing partner had given in to the demand from his father and Henry Booth to incorporate two chimneys into mainstream locomotive design; clearly he had felt obliged to comply and Michael Longridge advised him to ingratiate himself with the treasurer. Even if the two boiler / two chimney design, named the

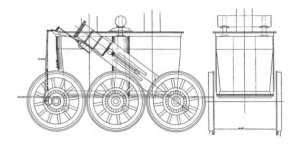

The Twin Sisters with two boilers and two chimneys

Twin Sisters, did burn coke effectively, it was hardly a fast traction prototype. The Canterbury & Whitstable Railway directors must now be persuaded to adopt locomotives. Indeed, the elder Stephenson specifically stipulated against them and a previous order of 1826 had been allowed to slip; Robert therefore had to do his utmost to regain confidence in his father's name. On 1 December 1828 Robert wrote to Michael Longridge:

'The boilers were shipped today... I have had two letters from Forman about the locomotive order and he has given us the order at last, but nothing can be done to it until I reach the manufactory.

I am really as anxious to be at Newcastle again as you can be to see me. I cannot say that I like Liverpool. Do not answer -'s letter until I see you...

... Ellis has got settled, and I have got up a proposal in my father's name, which is now before the directors of the Canterbury Railway Co. I expect at a general meeting... they will decide upon it. I cannot explain fully in a letter. I have thanked Mr Booth as you requested'.[25]

Although Robert remained loyal to RS&Co, keeping a tight rein on affairs and ensuring profitable returns, there is evidence to suggest that he sought a separate site in order to develop his progressive ideas as expressed in the *Lancashire Witch*. Michael Longridge had become his confidant and was sympathetic to the cause. So when Robert became engaged to Fanny in December 1828, he made arrangements for the wedding to take place as soon as possible, purchased a lease on one of Longridge's houses at Bedlington and even furnished the property. If Robert's intention was to build locomotives at the Iron Works, the threat worked; *'to this plan his father...and other friends were so adverse that he relinquished the scheme.'*[30] And there were to be no more false leads from Liverpool, only cover-up proposals and co-operation for the time being.

Again Robert rallied support from the Stephenson rival Timothy Hackworth, knowing this involvement would help to put pressure on a now desperate situation. It was a means of convincing a very stubborn father that his design ideas were right, thus ensuring the abolition of stationary engines on the L&MR at the Rainhill inclines. The locomotive superintendent wrote a lengthy reply giving detailed ammunition for their report concluding:

'Do not discompose yourself, my dear Sir; if you express your manly, firm, decided opinion, you have done your part as their adviser. And if it happened to be read some day in the newspapers - "Whereas the Liverpool and Manchester Railway has been strangled by ropes," - we shall not accuse you of guilt being accessory either before or after the fact'.[26]

The month of March 1829 was spent in London with Locke, giving evidence during the Newcastle & Carlisle Railway Bill proceedings. Both young engineers were unusually demonstrative about their experience and achievements. On 9 March the long awaited reports were submitted to the L&MR Board. Robert reacted two days later:

'The report of Walker and Rastrick has been received but it is in favour of fixed engines. We are preparing for a counter report in favour of locomotives which I believe still will ultimately get the day, but from present appearances nothing decisive can be said: rely upon it, locomotives shall not be cowardly given up. I will fight for them until the last. They are worthy of a conflict'.[31]

Being the better scribe, Locke wrote the counter-attack, their main argument being the locomotive's flexibility as an independent agent: *'we cannot but express our decided conviction that a system...could be entirely stopped by a single minor breakdown'.*[32] And declared stationary engines *'to be entirely unfitted for a public railway'.*[32] Other conclusions were also *'hotly contravened'*[33] in this joint production. Their *'careful reasonings'*[33] strengthened the desire for some directors *'to decide for locomotives'.*[33]

Returning to Liverpool in April, Locke was in a position to distribute their manuscript pamphlet and persuade individual directors, finding a particular champion in Richard Harrison. Indeed it was considered that because the Walker and Rastrick report had been so: *'...industriously circulated among the directors of the company, it might have been adopted had not Robert Stephenson and Joseph Locke stepped in and shown the insanity of the project. Their arguments, which subsequently took the form of a pamphlet decided the question in favour of the locomotive'.*[32]

Undoubtedly disappointed that both deputations ignored his Springwell locomotives, Locke stressed in this influential pamphlet how they could mount inclines *'which varied from 1 in 280 to 1 in 80'*[32] with only a single flue and blast pipe to stimulate the fire, thus producing a high-pressure power machine *'in order that simplicity and compactness may be achieved'*[32]. The pamphleteers' views were in fact *'diametrically opposed'*[32] to those of the elder Stephenson and Wood who had abandoned the blast as a means of economising on the fuel.

Despite Robert and Joseph's awareness of the possibility of much greater speeds from the envisaged boiler system, they diplomatically wrote in cautious terms during the spring of 1829: *'On a level railway, a locomotive engine weighing from four to five tons, will convey twenty tons of goods, exclusive of carriage at the rate of 12 miles an hour'.*[13]

The *Rocket*

As a consequence of their pamphlet, a premium of £500 was offered *'for an improved locomotive engine'*.[34] It is amazing how the 'Stipulations and Conditions' for the trials, announced on 25 April 1829 appeared as tailor-made for Robert's intentions; indeed they closely followed the wording of their pamphlet. The 'Premium Engine' had to be capable of drawing after it, day by day, a train of carriage of the gross weight of twenty tons, with a boiler pressure not exceeding 50lbs per square inch. It had to be supported on springs and the chimney not to exceed fifteen feet. Even a smaller locomotive was allowed if the weight was reduced to 4½ tons or under, when it could be placed on four wheels. *'The price must not exceed £500 and be delivered for trial at the Liverpool end on the railway not later than 1st of October next'*.[34]

Facing tremendous pressure, Henry Booth and George Stephenson agreed to finance Robert Stephenson's 'Premium Engine' entry. *'Keenly alive to the nature of the contest…Robert grappled with the task before him'*[35] of how to increase the heating surface of the boiler and achieve a white-hot furnace, as he walked from his lodgings in Charlotte Square to the RS&Co works. He devised a system whereby gases from a separate firebox surrounded by a water space would pass through numerous small tubes fitted in the boiler surrounded by water. As he expressed at the time: *'The effect of high-pressure is now almost universally admitted to depend, not so much on the size of cylinder as upon the quantity of steam which the boiler can generate and upon the degree of its elasticity'*.[32] This extensive heating surface would be the means of generating steam with unprecedented rapidity and thereby enabling travel at speed and mounting inclines without interrupting the journey for a change of motive power. This is just what the majority of the L&MR directors wanted.

Undoubtedly George Stephenson used his influence to secure a suitable house in

5 Greenfield Place, Newcastle upon Tyne

Newcastle for his son and bride-to-be. Ten minutes walk away from the factory, the six houses of Greenfield Place passed through John Dobson's Agency and number five had recently been completed; the magnificent views of Lord Ravensworth's estate and beyond can still be seen. The month of May would be spent furnishing this typical late Georgian house with a spacious first floor drawing room fitted with French windows and iron balconies. Fanny insisted on a sofa à la mode and her piano was shipped from London. *'The outskirts of Newcastle had few more pleasant places'*.[36] Robert could exercise his dog and horse on the vast public town moor to the north. Entered in the Robert Stephenson & Co. Ledger are his Newfoundland dog, which cost two pounds, a bay mare costing £23 15s 0d and six months rent for 5 Greenfield Place at £20.

His design intentions for the competition locomotive would only be partially solved due to the tight timescale. A highly specialised item, the separate firebox, was to be constructed in

Liverpool and for Robert not to have ensured its design and position as a workable proposition is inconceivable. In order to fulfil an order for the Canterbury & Whitstable Railway (C&WR), a locomotive was on the production line at RS & Co in 1826 consecutively with two for Springwell Colliery and built under Locke's auspices. For reasons of economy the parts would have been cast at the same time. Subsequently the C&WR decided against using locomotives. As production was very limited until Robert's return, the parts would have been available at RS & Co for use. In anticipation of a re-order from Canterbury, Robert could justifiably use this locomotive ordered by them for experimental purposes. The surviving drawings of this locomotive (later named *Invicta*)[37] are in Robert's hand and reveal a design that is at once outmoded in February 1830 but also experimental. For instance, the straight-sided rectangular and non-mainstream separate firebox is definite, as if already constructed. This straightforward design was within the capabilities of his workforce in May 1829, but the actual sophisticated firebox for the 'Premium Engine' is curved with an *'ogee finish'*[37] at the top and therefore had to be made by specialists. The drawing of this firebox in Robert's hand has survived.

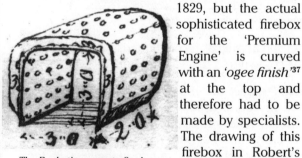

The Rocket's separate fire box, drawn by Robert

Obsessed with secrecy, the trial of the experimental locomotive with the fitted firebox intended for Canterbury probably took place at Springwell Colliery near Gateshead Fell, where Joseph Locke had strong links. By June Robert realised that his chances of success were high; he was on the brink of creating a locomotive design that would change the social and economic world forever. This concept, as well as his impending marriage, profoundly moved him and is reflected in a letter written on 6 June 1829: *'I was very much upset when I parted with*

you on Gateshead Fell. So many new feelings and novel reflections darted across my mind. The world would be materially changed. These sentiments you can appreciate more readily than I can describe them'.[38]

A bridge disaster on the L&MR probably prevented a Liverpool contingent being present at his wedding to Frances Sanderson, held at St Botolph Without Bishopsgate, London on Wednesday 17 June. A dominant presence of Fanny's relatives, their friends and associates was ominous. Key roles were to be occupied by some of them, at the factory and in his business affairs. Then the newly-weds spent a four day honeymoon in North Wales.

Returning to Greenfield Place, Robert Stephenson set the 'Premium Engine' production in motion straight away. George Phipps, the RS&Co. draughtsman, recalled this dedication. *'Punctual to a moment, and methodical to a nicety, the young engineer was always at his post, and ready for every emergency. No mishap found him unprovided with a remedy'.* Away from prying eyes, the full-scale drawing prior to construction was executed on the office floor. *'In making the drawings and calculations for the new engine,'* the Chief was assisted by Phipps who recalled with enthusiastic admiration:

'Having made the original drawings under Mr. Robert Stephenson, I can bear witness to the care and judgement bestowed by him upon every detail. In the arrangement of the tubes, with the method of securing their extremities, the detached firebox, and many other matters of detail, all requiring much consideration, Mr. Stephenson was well aided in all the mechanical details by the late Mr. William Hutchinson.

I may perhaps be allowed to add that in this and all other engineering works Mr Stephenson was always ready to avail himself of the abilities of those around him, his kindly consideration always eliciting the best fruits of their powers'.[41]

His mechanic since 1821 and conversant with day-to-day construction methods, Robert

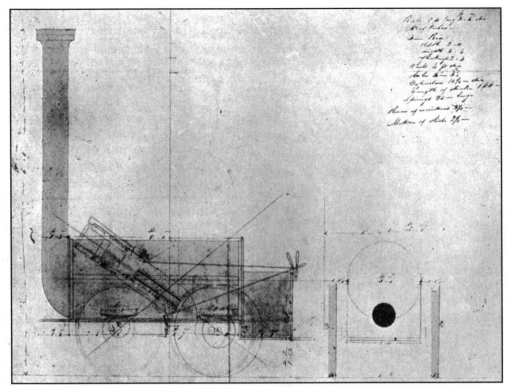

The Canterbury and Whistable locomotive, later called the 'Invicta'

cajoled the most out of Hutchinson by calling him an *'oracle'*.[40] By August, many of the component parts were completed and Robert was in a position to send polite, informed letters about his intentions to Henry Booth.

On 3 August, Robert Stephenson the designer wrote: *'The wheels I am arranging so as to throw 2 Tuns upon the large wheels in order to get friction upon the rail'.*[42] He borrowed the simple elegance of Trevithick's 1802 patent Steam Road Carriage with direct drive to the large pair of driving wheels and dispensed with the outside rods connecting the wheels, a component only necessary for heavy goods haulage. Fiercely competitive, Robert remarked of Timothy Hackworth's boiler:

'it is ingenious but it will not destroy the smoke with coal... he does not appear to understand that a coke fire will only burn briskly where the escape of the carbonic gas is immediate'.[43]

On 21 August, he continued to inform Booth, as co-owner:

'... I expect the mode of changing gear will please you; it is now as simple as I can make it and I believe effectual. The firebox is put into its place, but it is not quite square built which gives rise to a little apparent neglect in the workmanship. I have endeavoured to hide it as much as possible... please inform my father and Mr Locke the progress we have made'.[43]

There are no letters from Henry Booth and George Stephenson in Liverpool to the *Rocket's* designer in Newcastle. Keeping the 'Conditions and Stipulations' firmly in check, Robert Stephenson's only question is in this connection; *'Query therefore is it judicious to prove the boiler to 150lbs per square inch. I should say not!'*[43] The answer came from Joseph Locke as revealed in the last letter to Booth:

'Newcastle Tyne, Sept. 5th 1829. Dear Sir... On the whole the Engine is capable of doing as much if not more than set forth in the stipulations. After a great deal of trouble and anxiety we have got the tubes perfectly tight. As requested by you in Mr Locke's letter, I have not tried the boiler above 120lbs. On Friday next the Engine will leave by way of Carlisle and arrive in L'pool on Wednesday week'.[43]

Robert almost certainly got 'the tubes perfectly tight',[43] by expanding them into the tube plate. And Nicholas Wood was later prepared to reveal that the successful multitubular boiler was not the L&MR treasurer's idea: 'Mr Booth laid claim to the merit of having suggested to Mr Stephenson that... the application of more tubes might be useful. Stephenson however never admitted that this communication was of any assistance to him in the adoption of the multitubular principle of tubes and outside firebox'.[44] That there were two fireboxes associated with the Premium Engine soon to be called the Rocket has led to much confusion and speculation. Indeed Wood's drawing of the Rocket's firebox is reminiscent to that shown on the Invicta.

In the immediate aftermath of success, Henry Booth had to justify the £100 gift from the L&MR to develop a 'method of producing Steam without Smoke'.[21] Despite the fact that Booth's known suggested ideas stopped with the Twin Sisters, his name was allowed to be carved in stone even by the two young engineers, Robert Stephenson and Joseph Locke. They were grateful for the patronage; Locke conceded 'with great reluctance'.[45] Their Report, distributed to the directors in April 1829, was published in February 1830. George Stephenson even attempted to insist 'that the title page should bear his name and his name only'.[43] The text of their first manuscript had an added section which brought it up-to-date with the Rainhill Trials. 'The Report drawn up by Joseph Locke and Robert Stephenson had demonstrated theoretically the superiority of the locomotive and the Rocket proved it'.[45]

The Rainhill Trials: 6 - 14 October 1829

Locke likened the Rainhill Trials to the St Leger, with tents for the ladies, a band to entertain and stands for spectators. Of the many entrants, there were only three main contestants: 'The Rocket of Mr Robt. Stephenson of Newcastle; the Novelty of Messrs. Braithwaite & Ericsson of London and the Sans Pareil of Mr. Hackworth of Darlington'.[46] The Liverpool Courier recorded on the 7 October 1829: 'Never, perhaps, on any previous occasion, were so many scientific gentleman and practical engineers collected together on one spot'.[46]

The Rocket performed admirably on the 6th and 8th of October, the Novelty equally well on the 6th, but suffered a broken pipe on 10th. By the 13th October Sans Pareil was finally ready. Even though overweight, it was allowed to do the 70 mile trial pulling three times its weight. After 25 miles one of the feed-pipes burst. Then on the 14th Novelty's boiler 'yielded to the high temperature to which it was exposed'[46] after completing only 3 miles. On 16th October John Dixon wrote a graphic account to his brother James:

'The Rocket is by far the best Engine I have ever seen for Blood and Bone united. Story will give you particulars...Timothy has been very sadly out of temper ever since he came...he openly accused all GS's people of conspiring to hinder him...he got many trials but never got half of his 70 miles done'.[46]

He goes on to describe the springless Sans Pareil as 'very ugly and Boiler runs not very much, he had to feed her with more Meal and Malt Sprouts than would fatten a pig'...[46] Likening Novelty to a 'Tea Urn with a Parlour like appearance' but on every trial 'it had some mishap'.[46]

After the prize of £500 was presented to the owners and the designer of the Rocket, four more locomotive engines were ordered by

𝕸echanics' 𝕸agazine,

MUSEUM, REGISTER, JOURNAL, AND GAZETTE.

No. 324.]   SATURDAY, OCTOBER 24, 1829.   [Price 3*d*.

" THE ROCKET," LOCOMOTIVE STEAM ENGINE OF
MR. ROBERT STEPHENSON.

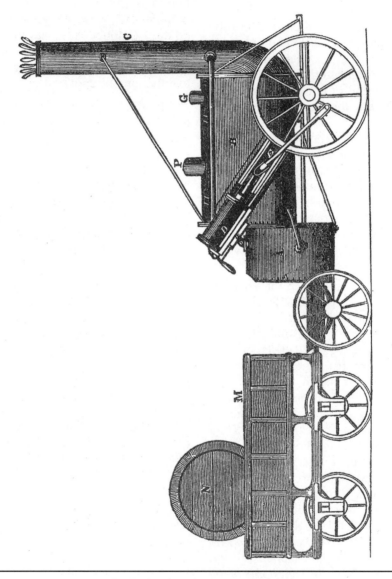

[The earliest known contemporary illustration of the 'Rocket']

'The Rocket' from 'Mechanics Magazine'

the L&MR. Robert Stephenson now had an opportunity to achieve an outside cylinder prototype in stages, resulting in the *Northumbrian*, which arrived in Liverpool on 9 August 1830 and *'created something of a sensation'* with *'a boiler and chimney of copper instead of iron'*.[47] The firebox was now an integral part of the boiler and the frame to carry the cylinders horizontally consisted of wrought iron plates. He stated almost 30 years later:

'From the date of running the Rocket on the Liverpool and Manchester Railway, the locomotive engine has received many minor improvements in detail, and especially in accuracy of workmanship; but in no essential particular does the existing locomotive differ from that which obtained the prize of the celebrated competition at Rainhill'.[48]

At the time, he wished to fulfil his objective and place the cylinders *'beneath the boiler entirely'*[2]; the *Rocket* was just part of his design process. In February 1830, for the first time Robert showed an alternative intention on the *Invicta* drawing, to place the cylinders at the *'smokebox end'*,[49] driving the back wheels. Again he was using the locomotive as an experiment. This position was necessary because cylinders placed horizontally inside the wheels would have gone through the firebox: an impossibility. Indeed his specific aim was to conserve heat by positioning the cylinders directly below an intended smoke box. However, he had to take the outside cylinder locomotive to its logical conclusion first and his systematic development stages were not yet complete. Being so successful in this task, to about turn and begin an expensive design process all over again was daunting.

THE LOCOMOTIVE STEAM ENGINES
Which competed for the Prize of £500 offered by the Directors of the Liverpool and Manchester Railway Compy.— drawn to a Scale ¼ inch to a foot

The **ROCKET** *of Mr. Robt. Stephenson of Newcastle*
Which drawing a load equivalent to three times its weight travelled at the rate of 12¼ miles an hour, & with a carriage & passengers at the rate of 24 miles. Cost per mile for fuel about three halfpence

The **NOVELTY** *of Messrs. Braithwaite & Erricsson of London.*
Which drawing a load equivalent to three times its weight, travelled at the rate of 20¼ miles an hour, & with a Carriage & Passengers at the rate of 32 miles. Cost per mile for fuel about one halfpenny

The **SANS PAREIL** *of Mr Hackworth of Darlington*
Which drawing a load equivalent to three times its weight, travelled at the rate of 12¼ miles an hour — Cost for fuel per mile about two-pence.

[from the Mechanics' Magazine, Vol. XII., 28th November 1829.]

The three main entrants, 'Rocket, Novelty and Sans Pareil'

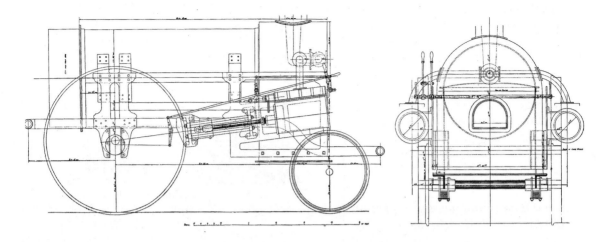

'Northumbrian', drawing of about June 1830

In May 1830, a friend congratulated him on his success and received the heartfelt reply: *'I can assure you I sometimes feel very uneasy about my position. My courage at times almost fails me; and I fear that some fine morning my reputation may break under me like an egg-shell'.*[50] Crack he did not. His consummate experience of engines gave him the necessary confidence to resist the fiercely held antagonism against crank axles and take a risk both to his reputation and finances in order to create an efficient locomotive.

Action would have to be taken swiftly before the outside cylinder type became an accepted norm. In order to produce a six-wheel, inside cylinder prototype he must be able to secure orders and operate these locomotives under his charge in order to detect design problems as they became apparent. Freedom as an independent agent had to be a realistic option at this crucial time. To juxtapose financial independence and have a necessary railway outlet outside George Stephenson & Son took tremendous strength of purpose, especially for a man duty-bound to his co-partners, with a deep affection for one

of them. A patriarchal position was inevitably dominant, Robert Stephenson had also to resist an only parent with a suffocating influence during his developing years.

Inside cylinder development

Robert's great determination to pursue an alternative design course was again supported by Michael Longridge, who acted as a broker. Concepts for a four-wheel inside cylinder locomotive were on the drawing board by July 1830, while his final outside cylinder stage, the *Northumbrian* was being constructed. But not until October did the magnificent crank-axled locomotive named *Planet* make a debut on the L&MR. This style of locomotive resulted from the pressure of competition.

Inevitably a challenge came from Timothy Hackworth, aware of the design friction between the Stephensons. In an attempt to avoid Robert's boiler system and maintain a design stance, he ordered a locomotive with a Napier-type boiler and inside cylinders early in 1830 but was not completed at RS&Co until October. The clerk Harris Dickinson wrote: *'Hackworth's engine has been tried, and works very well, but I am afraid there will be a deficiency in her powers of generating steam'.*[51] The question does arise: was there a purposeful delay to the manufacture of this locomotive, called the *Globe*? In no way would Robert Stephenson allow the Stockton & Darlington engine superintendent any priority to his intentions declared on the 1 January 1828. The *Globe* proved to be the first and last of its type. Robert clearly did not benefit or derive ideas from his rival's drawings received in March 1830: *'a comparison between the two will show that, beyond the common use of a crank axle, there was no resemblance in either general arrangements of parts, details of construction, or appearance'.*[51]

However, the Liverpool firm of engine manufacturers Bury, Curtis & Kennedy did prove to be a very serious threat. Having worked at RS&Co. for eighteen months 1824-5, James Kennedy gained expertise in locomotive production, and by 1830 had realised the possible performance advantage arising from an inside cylinder design. For offering the enginewright these opportunities, Robert expressed an unmitigated anger to his father: *'if Kennedy had not obtained a great deal of information from us here, we should have stood much higher as Locomotive Engine Makers than we do now - Bury never would have made an Engine'.*[52] In midsummer 1830 Kennedy's firm pressed their wares on to the L&MR directors. Inevitably the engineer was unsuccessful in his attempt to resist this intrusion: *'The reasons of the dispute are no doubt to be found in George Stephenson's fears of broken crank axles'.*[53] Robert could now argue for an equal opportunity: hence the *Planet*.

During a later heated row, Robert Stephenson declared how 'the working drawings of the *Planet*...had been made and the engine constructed under my direction without reference'[54] to Bury, Curtis & Kennedy's first locomotive named *Liverpool*. The RS&Co. Chief went on to defend his stance:

'These facts could be fully confirmed by those who were confidentially employed upon the engine at the time. Neither was there any analogy between the two machines, for the Planet had a multitubular boiler, the fire being urged by a blast pipe, and the cylinders which were as nearly horizontal as their position would permit, were fixed inside, or between the frames, because

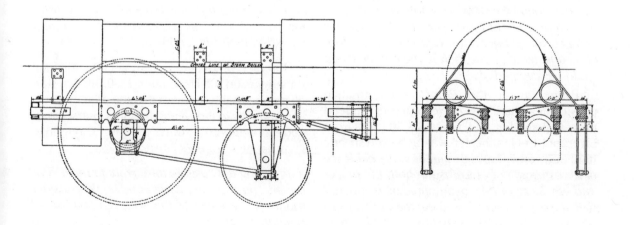

Planet-type frames

it was only by such an arrangement that they could be placed within the smoke box, where it was considered desirable to fix them, in order to prevent the condensation of the steam in the cylinders, and the consequent loss of power'.[54]

The success of the *Planet* which arrived in Liverpool on 4 October 1830, had much to do with Robert's outside wooden frame, strengthened by iron plates and angles which *'formed a completed rectangle'.*[55] Inner wooden frames also served to support the crank axle, thus relieving it from undue stresses, and carried the slide bars as well; attached to the front inner frame by means of angle irons and screws were the cylinders. Two years later one of the L&MR directors wrote of the *Planet*: *'She came nearer to what was considered perfection, relatively of course, than any which had succeeded her'.*[56] But at one of her trials, on 29 November 1830 *Planet* was reduced to hauling a goods train, *'the freight weight being 51 tons 1 cwt; the Gross weight including Engine, Tender, Waggons and some passengers about 80 tons'.*[57] Additional engines had to assist up the inclines and a journalist remarked:

'We understand that the journey on Saturday would have been performed in less time, had not the engineer, when passing over Chat Moss, allowed the fire to burn too low, and afterwards, when he found the steam was falling off, thrown a large quantity of coke upon it, which greatly reduced the temperature, and caused the loss of a considerable time, before the proper speed could be regained'.[57]

Even though the *Planet's* performance possibilities had been recognised, indeed proven at another trial, when the 30 miles from Liverpool to Manchester was achieved in one hour and consistent high speeds were *'evidence of an extraordinary increase in both the power and efficiency of this locomotive, as compared with its predecessors'*,[57] Planet-type locomotives ordered by the L&MR in October 1830 had to be reallocated to Robert's Warrington & Newton and the Garnkirk & Glasgow railways. These rejections by the L&MR show the influence of some of their key players and does much to explain Robert's motivation for independent outlets.

However, a demand *'for a more powerful locomotive to be used on the incline plane'*[58] from L&MR directors led to an order and gave Robert an opportunity to send two more 'Planet' types by stealth. They had expected an outside cylinder 'Phoenix' type early in 1831, but he developed a coupled wheel variation with larger dimensions and the L&MR got an outside cylinder 0-4-0 instead. His *'Design of an Engine to be called Goliath for the Liverpool Incline Plane'*[58] has survived. Doodles of daffodil heads form a top border, a necessary variation from intense concentration. The twin locomotive *Samson* was later fitted with iron wheels and weighed about 10 tons, thus almost doubling the adhesive capacity of the *Planet*. Despite this success, the trend of many RS&Co. orders from the L&MR having to be reallocated, continued.

To pursue what he considered to be correct design development, he intended to establish a new locomotive factory with the Warrington-based iron founder Charles Tayleur. At the onset he gave the excuse of 'having been applied to by some Parties in Liverpool to commence a Manufactory there',[59] *but the astute RS & Co. partners knew that the motivation came from Robert to extend 'his own interest'*[59] *and that it was 'decidedly his sentiments'.*[59]

He first broached the subject to Michael Longridge on 13 December 1830, at the start of some doubts concerning the Planet-type's acceptability to the L&MR directors. Subsequent correspondence shows how Longridge championed Robert's cause:

'I am going to Glasgow tomorrow to meet your father... In the meantime you should consider maturely the effect of the proposal you intend making to Mr Pease. The establishment you contemplate at Liverpool appears to me fraught with injury to Forth Street... My own individual

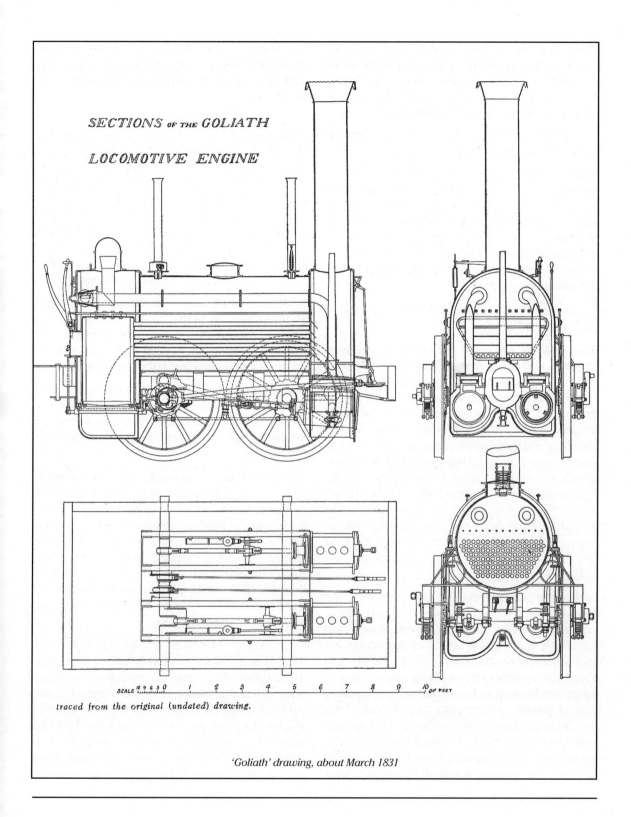

SECTIONS OF THE GOLIATH

LOCOMOTIVE ENGINE

SCALE 12 9 6 3 0   1   2   3   4   5   6   7   8   9   10 OF FEET

traced from the original (undated) drawing.

'Goliath' drawing, about March 1831

Interest is so very small, that it cannot be put into competition with yours, and I therefore only mention it that you may clearly understand that whatever Mr Pease and Mr Richardson determine upon, I shall be guided by'.[59]

Michael Longridge then wrote to Edward Pease 22 December 1830:

'When I last saw Robert Stephenson, he mentioned to me his having been applied to by some parties in Liverpool to commence a Manufactory there... I am now on my way to London... and propose being at Darlington by the Mail on Tuesday night the 28th inst. and shall be glad to visit Mr Thomas Richardson and you the following day'.[59]

Edward Pease replied to Michael Longridge on 9 March 1831:

'Two or three days ago my cousin Richardson handed me thy letter to him containing a copy of Rob. Stephenson's to thee relative to engaging in another concern at Liverpool for the making of Locomotives... it seems decidedly R's sentiments... should RS think it hard that we should stand in the way of his advancement in Life... - who has acted most generously to him? who has used every effort to exalt him? & make him what he is as to his standing in the World? & humanly estimating events, where and what would he have been without us: either as an engineer or as a scientific man? in what field has he developed his talents? often to our cost in Forth street'.[60]

Robert Stephenson did not approach the Quaker cousins face-to-face. Edward Pease continued: *'I called in Broad Street, Robert had left the evening before: he had not conversed with Richardson on the subject'.* Pease and Richardson knew nothing about engineering or iron manufacture; but time had proved Robert's design policies to be right in the past. They would recall how disadvantaged their factory was between June 1826 and December 1827 and how it might be adversely affected again. Establishing another locomotive factory near

to Liverpool was a means to an end, and the strength of Robert's conviction, as expressed in a letter to Michael Longridge, helped to reassure his partners:

'Newcastle, 7 Mar. 1831
Should I had become connected with another Manufactory for building Engines in Lancashire, or elsewhere, I have no objection to bind myself to devote an equal share of my time and attention to the existing establishment at Newcastle. I will also pledge myself not to hold a larger interest in any other Factory, than I have in Forth Street, and to divide the Locomotive Engine orders equally.

> *Robt. Stephenson.'*[59]

After prolonged discussions, Robert Stephenson's partners finally agreed to his wishes. One of the resolutions made at the RS&Co. meeting held on 27 June 1831 was to agree to a new factory on the condition:

'- That the Firm at Liverpool should be Charles Tayleur, Junr. & Co., or at any other Firm not embracing the name of 'Stephenson' so as to distinguish it entirely from the Newcastle House'.[59]

The threat of forming an independent factory would be sufficient to show his resolve to instigate the production of inside cylinder locomotives. Indeed, demands for increased power at a time when the strength of rails were limited, inevitably meant an increase from four to six wheels. Predictably, once having secured this objective within a few years, Robert *'retired from the said firm'*.[61] The motivation for being involved at all had ceased.

Robert Stephenson resolve to take risks regarding locomotive development gave him an arrogant air. Indeed his prodigious audacity was noted in contrast to his father's more easy-going nature. For instance when George Washington Whistler visited from the USA, he noted that the younger Stephenson talked in highfaluting terms and gave an air of impressing people. Fortunately some Americans, such as

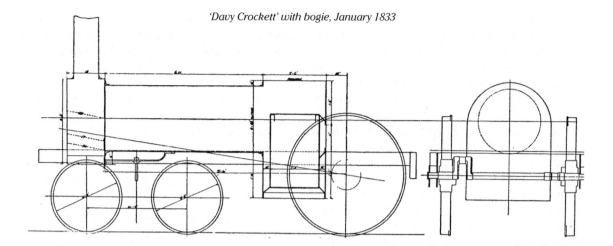

'Davy Crockett' with bogie, January 1833

the Stevens family, accepted his confidence as representing the certainty of knowledge. Locomotive orders for the USA from 1828–36 were in abundance and without the restrictions placed upon him by a conservative father, Robert's initiative reign supreme. Conditions in the USA led to innovations such as the bogie to accommodate excessive curves which already existed in their extensive railroads. As early as 1828, *'Robert Stephenson recommended to a deputation of American engineers visiting Newcastle…a track for working the curves of 400 feet radius'.*[62] Also the working or *'valve gear of his first bogie'*[62] locomotive was considered an advance *'since the eccentric rod drives in the backward direction on to a rocking lever placed below the foot plate, and therefore easy of access to the engineman…Another interesting feature is the anticipation of the driving wheel arrangement afterwards adopted and patented by Thomas Crampton'.*[62] By 1835 *'three six-wheeled locomotives with four-wheeled bogies'* were being built for the South Carolina railroad. Both the adoption of the bar frame introduced on his 1828 *America* and of a circular firebox with domed top for *'Mr Stevens' Locomotive, New York, America 1831'*, led to a general type. It was recognised by contemporaries that Robert Stephenson had provided a locomotive prototype for both sides of the Atlantic and was

'fond of winning others to his opinions'.[63]

In September 1832, with *'a transcendent capacity for taking trouble',*[64] Robert Stephenson personally ordered a six wheel, inside cylinder single driving wheel locomotive to power passenger trains, later called the *Patentee*. This move, together with the ability to manufacture locomotives of his choice at the Vulcan Foundry, might induce George Stephenson at least to give him tacit consent. Renowned for only taking calculated risks, Robert needed to have an independent railway under his charge. Not surprisingly, another six-wheel locomotive variation entitled *'Proposed Engine for the Stanhope Railway'* is dated October 1832.

His appointment as Consultant Engineer to the Stanhope & Tyne mineral line with personnel from Broad Street, London, came at the same time. To an increasing extent he relied on his wife's family and associates for support; yet he also gives the impression of seeking his father's approval. The correspondence between father and son should not be misread. In order to involve George and to get his own way, the young engineer dissembled. He did not have a delicate disposition; but on 24 September 1832 he wrote:

'My dear Father, I would have replied to your last letter sooner but I have been a little unwell… In

a few days and I shall be able to get out and take exercise which will soon bring me round again: but I should like to see you down here for a few days as I want to talk to you on several subjects, particularly the Stanhope and Tyne Railway for which they have appointed me the consulting engineer at £300 per annum - There are several stationary Engines to be erected and there is one I want to have your opinion upon, as the application of an Engine in the manner that I propose is entirely new and I want you to see the situation - Do therefore come down and spend a few days with me - I am not in very good spirits and would like your company for a little time...It will not I hope interfere with the works at the Colliery your visit to Newcastle'...[65]

A way to his father's approval was to keep him content via a money spinning business proposition and involve George's influential railway director friends as well, even though Robert had expressed a *'dislike'* of Liverpool and some of the city's Railway directors in league with his father. On one occasion he had been forced to resurvey:

'...a railway which I have got the management of near Bolton... so as to reduce the expense, even at the risk of having a less advisable line. This is one way of doing things, but proud as I am I must submit. I have tried in my cool and solitary moments to look with patience on such proceedings, but, by heavens, it requires a greater store than I have. I would patiently hear this alteration if they did it from principle; but, knowing, and indeed hearing them say from what the alteration does really spring, I cannot but consider it unworthy of Liverpool merchants'.[66]

At base, Robert Stephenson's entrepreneurial instincts could be just as strong as his father's. By effective persuasion he enticed Booth, Sandars and others to invest in Leicester and Swannington Railway shares knowing that the railway passed over an extremely rich coal seam in the vicinity of Snibston. And when a nearby estate came up for auction early in 1831, Robert persuaded his father, Joseph Sandars and Sir Joshua Walmsley to purchase it, thus becoming owners of a very lucrative mining concern: hence his hope that George's visit to Newcastle would not interfere with works at the Colliery. He had hoped to keep his father content, being in charge of a highly productive pit. But George continued to make his presence felt at railway board meetings; nor did the influential Henry Booth give the required support for locomotives, let alone a six-wheel, inside cylinder type.

On 1 July 1832 Robert wrote a letter to the Leicester & Swannington Railway Company about the powers and capabilities of his locomotives; over a year later he took the risk of designating his 'fourth' six-wheel 'Planet'-type to this railway, labelling the drawing 'Locomotive for the Leicester & Swannington Railway, September 1833'.[67] Then on 26 November, he influenced a friend and committee member, John Ellis, to report to the Board of being *'authorised by Mr.Robert Stephenson to say that a six wheel Engine of great power...would be ready in a week; and if the Directors think it right to order it, it might be sent off at once...Resolved that an order be given for the Engine'.[68]* So sure was he in his conviction of the virtues offered by an inside cylinder type, Robert took the risk of manufacturing without the certainty of an order. This is how he operated in a tight squeeze. With factory expansion as well, RS&Co. occupied land and buildings by private arrangements long before legal documents were in place.

The London & Birmingham Railway

An agreement between the London & Birmingham Railway Company (L&BR) and George Stephenson & Son (GS&Son) had been signed on 18 September 1830, but in order to test and develop his proposed six-wheeled locomotive prototype to power passenger trains at speed, it was the younger Stephenson who *'zealously'*[69] fought for the post of Engineer-in-

Chief. The Bill was thrown out in 1832; Robert was *'no exception to the rule that envy is the shadow of success'.*[70] Fortunately, serving as Chairman of the Committee, his former employer Lord Wharncliffe gave him reassuring support:

'My young friend, don't take this to heart. The decision is against you; but you have made such a display of power that your future is made for life'.[70]

The 'Age of Enlightenment' was drawing to a close, consequently both Stephensons benefited from the prevailing philosophies of this era which had thrown off the trappings of class and gave them opportunities to succeed, far more than any future legal reforms or education for all. A grateful Robert Stephenson remained a Tory.

After painstaking attention to detail, Robert's hard work came to fruition during the next year. Three weeks after incorporation on 28 May 1833, he received an unofficial letter from one of the L&BR secretaries: *'Nothing is said as to the appointment of engineer, but I think you may be easy on that head'.*[69] The experienced and respected engineer John Rastrick praised Robert's work to the Board:

'Let nothing deter you from executing the work in the most substantial manner and on the most scientific principles so that it may serve as a model for all future railways and become the wonder and admiration of Posterity'.[72]

Despite being dismissed as being 'still young - very young - to be engineer-in-chief to such an undertaking'[71] and by some who *'honestly mistrusted young genius',*[71] others were impressed by his energy, his detailed plans and declared engineering intentions; thus he earned the respect of most of the L&BR directors.

Locomotive for the Leicester and Swannington railway, September 1833

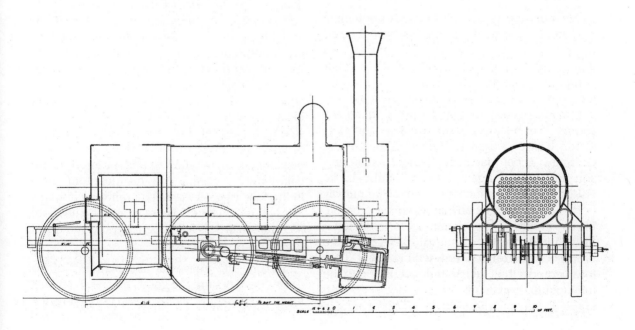

Preparations to leave Newcastle upon Tyne

During the past five years, the RS&Co. workforce had pulled together under the total commitment of their Chief. Even his social life revolved around the staff's well-being. Close friends remembered the happy times *'spent in Greenfield Place with music, talk and cigars. To these evening parties the pupils at the works were frequently invited'.*[73] Being an apprentice at the prestigious locomotive works was a highly sought position and in order to limit numbers, Robert Stephenson had to increase the premium. On 11 July 1833 he wrote to Thomas Richardson from Dieppe: *'I look forward to the London and Birmingham Railway going on. Taking young men, although it may be a profitable part of our business, is one that incurs great responsibility'.*[73] During his forthcoming absence he was to:

'...regret having made any arrangements for allowing some of them into the offices, to become acquainted in every detail with our plans etc. They have no sooner done so, that they leave and come away with what has cost us a great deal of money and more thought'.[73]

He must now protect his interest by obtaining a 'Patent Specification' of his six-wheeled locomotive. The trend of RS&Co.'s orders from the L&MR having to be reallocated to other companies continued. Robert's prototype locomotive only survived because these railway companies were either, as he put it *'under my charge'*,[74] or because of his overseas contracts in the USA and then in Belgium, France and Germany. Accompanied by Michael Longridge's son James and agent Edward Starbuck, he visited European countries to advocate railway network advantages and in so doing promote his locomotives. The eighteen year old's letter from Frankfurt dated 11 August 1833 describes a dramatic occurrence worth writing about. They intercepted a thief taking their goods tied to the back of the coach:

'On returning to the carriage, we found a little basket of Mr Stephenson's turned upside down and the things all deranged...Stephenson roared out "get down you rascal" - we had no arms of any sort but made up our minds to have a fight - Starbuck took his walking stick and an umbrella tied together - Stephenson a roller that our prints were on...if the worst came to the worst it would be a game of fisticuffs... An honest innkeeper came and promised to make us as comfortable as he could...We then gave the carriage up to the police and this morning came on here. Starbuck has gone to the Consul with whom he is acquainted to ask his opinion.'[75]

Being an excellent linguist, Starbuck proved to be an invaluable foreign Agent. Their hard work paid off, railway consultancy posts followed together with locomotive orders. Robert Stephenson wrote in his notebook at the date 30 September 1833 - *'signed the contract with the London and Birmingham directors, before Mr Barker at the Hummums, Covent Gardens. Dined with Stanhope directors'.*

On 7 October he took out a locomotive patent in his own name, Specification 6484.[76] It consists of four variations on his six-wheel 'Planet' type. In order to avoid the severe strain on the crank axle he removed the flanges from the driving wheels. Also his former practices are incorporated into this patent such as the multitubular boiler with integral firebox, smoke box, the blast to stimulate the fire, steel leaf springs, working gear, double frames to support inside cylinders and his latest invention, the steam brake. At last his 2-2-2 locomotive, ordered personally over a year before, was dispatched to the L&MR and ordered to be called the *Patentee*.[77] Was this meant as a slap in the face to a very reluctant railway company and to their engineer? There were to be no more locomotive orders for Robert Stephenson & Co. from the L&MR directors.

Despite the 'universal acceptance'[78] of his 'Patentee' type and the goods engine 0-6-0 built for the Leicester & Swannington becoming 'the maid of all work of the British railway',[79] Robert

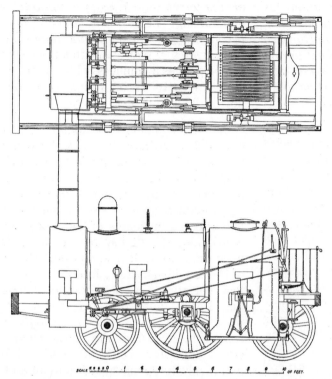

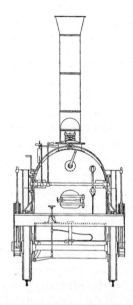

complained bitterly: *'Rivals are coming into the field who have not had to begin by expensive experiments. There is now no groping in the dark, at least there ought not to be'*.[73] He borrowed, adapted and created anew.

As an extremely loyal employee, Robert Stephenson intended to take his draughtsman George Phipps with him to work in a position of responsibility on theL&BR. Dividing the 111 mile line into six districts, each would require *'a confidential assistant at each place'*[11] thus ensuring that his *'plans are carefully and strictly attended to'*.[11] Other chosen assistant engineers included the more senior George Buck, the mining engineer Frank Forster and former RS&Co. apprentices, John Cass Birkinshaw and Thomas Gooch.

Whereas Robert himself had acted in authority as a railway engineer since 1821,

his team was inexperienced. Devoid of large-scale constructional precedents, all railway works in 1833, *'engaged the very anxious care of those who had the responsibility of designing them'*.[80] Unable therefore to take the initiative themselves, all his employees obeyed his detailed instructions initially and even at the end of his career, employees acknowledged working *'under Robert Stephenson's direction'*.[81] Contractors also had to abide by his dictate: there was not to be any *'deviation without full permission of the Engineer-in-Chief'*.[82]

A junior member of his team recalled Robert Stephenson's *'energetic countenance, frank bearing and falcon-like glance... he charmed all who came into contact with him. Kind and considerate to his subordinate, he was not without occasional outbursts of fierce northern passion... He knew how to attract people to him: he knew also how to be a firm and persistent hater'*,[84] that is of those who left his fold, uttered indiscretions and took Robert's know how with them. Another contemporary confirmed his *'magnetic power... and retaining through life, the affectionate devotion of those whom he once employed; it is not therefore surprising to find Mr Phipps's career intimately connected with that of Robert Stephenson'.*[42] The locomotive draughtsman's loyalty was worth more than his line drawing expertise at RS&Co.

By October 1833, Robert Stephenson's future intentions were in place, both with the stupendous task of constructing the London & Birmingham Railway and at his Works, where written communications twice a week and a few annual visits would have to suffice. *'Had circumstance left him free to follow his own inclination, Robert Stephenson, instead of taking a conspicuous position in London Society, would have passed his life at Newcastle in comparative retirement'.*[83] It was with sadness that he left Robert Stephenson & Co. having had the daily creative process at his fingertips. *'Intensely fond of the mechanical part of his profession'*,[83] he continually expressed his regret at having left Greenfield Place and wished to be remembered for his achievements while living there, even though he was to be lauded as *'the most successful civil engineer of his time'.*[83]

Postscript

Major decision making is complex. The Stephensons' reasons for moving to the capital must have been numerous. Fanny would be glad to be near her family and friends again. Both Stephensons, father and son, had a reputation for being titular chiefs, the L&BR determined not to allow this option. Robert was officially unable to divide his attention between projects if he wished to be Engineer-in-chief of the first Metropolitan railway in the world, even though his reluctance to leave the helm of a locomotive factory was profound. Even a few years later doubts still lingered in Robert's mind. Michael

Longridge attempted to reassure him: *'I feel very solicitous that you should devote the whole of your faculties underividedly to this magnificent undertaking [L&BR]; this being once well accomplished, your name and future are built upon a Rock'.*[84] Well aware that the locomotive prototype was a pointless achievement without a railway network on which to operate, the advice did not fall on stony ground.

Senior engineers may flounder and fail to build railways of magnitude. Doubts would lead to a lack of investment and dampen enthusiasm in the face of forever improving road and canal networks. Robert Stephenson had a duty to set precedents for others to follow. Gifted and capable engineers of his own generation would almost certainly rise to the occasion; even though I. K. Brunel had not yet emerged onto the railway scene, Joseph Locke fell into this category. Contemporaries recognised that Locke *'possessed peculiar qualities of mind which secured for him the confidence of capitalists, by whom the construction of the Grand Junction was entrusted to him'.*[85] Reared in a highly competitive environment and to be a sound businessman, Robert knew that the railway industry could be highly lucrative. He would remain at the forefront of the railway engineering. That meant being in London, the hive of activity.

'Had circumstance left him free'...[83] Due to the elder Stephenson's intransigence, an irreconcilable rift was firmly established between George Stephenson and Joseph Locke in 1833. Robert had the unenviable task of protecting his father's image yet retain an unflinching friendship with Joseph. Given an affable scenario within the auspices of GS & Son, the other chief engineer may well have preferred to leave major railway construction to this firm, playing a supportive role as before. As it was, only the advent of an economic slump in 1841 enabled Robert Stephenson time to focus his attention on locomotive design again. Aiming to improve the power by increasing the

boiler dimensions and to produce an effective *'working gear'*, he obtained a locomotive patent[86] in his own name on 23 June 1841.

Frances Stephenson's death on 4 October 1842 took away 'half his power of enjoying success'.[87] Perhaps as a means of overcoming grief, he became protective of Robert Stephenson & Co's interests, expanding the site and securing leases for the foreseeable future. Previously he had encouraged other factories to build his Patentee-types, indeed in 1836 he even suggested: *'I think it is worth considering whether Forth Street may not be offered to the Bedlington Co'.*[73] Now he ensured the prosperity of RS & Co with his highly successful 1841 *'Long Boiler'*[86] patent locomotive; while other firms laid off hands, RS&Co prospered. His financial manager wrote: *'The talk here is that the Hawthorns have little or nothing to do'.*[88]

'The year 1844 is a conspicuous landmark in the career of Robert Stephenson'.[89] Even though *'he found himself in the first rank of his profession, had he died then, he would have left nothing to which history would point as the monument of original and distinctive genius and he had raised the locomotive by a series of beautiful improvements from the ill proportioned and ineffective machine of 1828'*[89] almost to perfection. Contemporaries considered that his *'original and distinctive'*[89] achievement was the development of the tubular girder. This *'great innovation in constructive art, which has since been extended to architectural construction with the greatest success, was at first viewed with great distrust'.*[90] By authorising extensive experiments and calculations, Robert Stephenson gave civil engineering a scientific status. A colleague stated: *'To the genius which designed and executed the Britannia and Conway Bridges on the tubular principle, at a time when the use of wrought iron for large beams was nearly unknown, the engineering world is indebted, for important and profound investigations into the properties of wrought-iron beams'.*[91]

Locke publicly acknowledged that wrought iron plates riveted together had 'been used very long'[92] as load bearing frames on steam engines. The source of Robert Stephenson's expertise lay with locomotive development. He remained most proud of his *'early professional triumphs; to the last no part of his cares afforded him more pleasure than the direction of the Newcastle factory'.*[93]

Robert Stephenson's Long Boiler-type locomotive

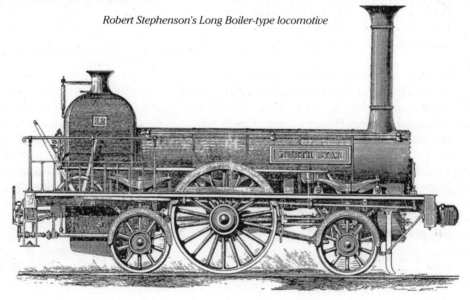

Robert Stephenson 1803 - 59 CHRONOLOGY

[Quotations, names of locomotives & ships are in italics]

1803   16 October: Robert Stephenson born at Willington Quay, a few miles east of Newcastle upon Tyne, where his father George (1781 - 1848) holds the post of brakesman for the ballast engine.
His parents rent one upper room in a terrace by the river.

1804   February: the first railway trips made by Richard Trevithick's 'Pen-y-darran' steam locomotive hauling both iron and passengers on cast iron tram plates.

- Trevithick, the inventor of the high-pressure steam engine, visits the Stephenson household and *nurses young Bobby many a time*.
- George Stephenson obtains a job at West Moor pit Killingworth, owned by the Grand Allies: the Earl Strathmore, Sir Thomas Liddell & the Rt. Hon. James Stuart-Wortley-Mackenzie, the largest mining consortium in Great Britain. During the winter of 1804/5 the Stephenson family move to Paradise Row, West Moor where the Killingworth waggonway runs by their garden to the staiths on the River Tyne.

1805   1 May: Trevithick's locomotive is demonstrated at Gateshead on smooth wooden rails.

- 3 August: sister Frances dies, three weeks after her birth.

1806   14 May: mother Frances dies.

- Father accepts a job in Montrose, Scotland and twenty year old Ann Snaith, from nearby Longbenton, is left to care for Robert.

1808   26 March: Ann marries his uncle Robert. They take the four year old boy with them to their new home.

- George returns to Killingworth; resumes his post as a brakesman and sets up a contracting business to repair low-pressure stationary engines; takes Robert back to Paradise Row.
- July: Trevithick's *Catch-me-who-can* locomotive, with single driving wheels, hauls passengers on a circular track near Euston Square, London. This engine is to be a direct influence on Robert's future locomotive development intentions.

I have attended to machinery all my life: Robert Stephenson.

Robert's earliest recollections were helping his father make model engines and repair engine parts. The precocious child offered opinions of his own and called one enginewright a *fool*.

c1810   Robert goes to school in Longbenton and is taught by parish clerk, Tommy Rutter. He earns pennies taking miner's picks to be sharpened at Longbenton's smithy.

Poverty, a mother of invention: Robert Stephenson

1811   The Napoleonic Wars drag on, horses are scarce and the transport of coal is almost at a standstill. Northern colliery owners ask their engineers (called viewers or agents) to devise locomotives on the waggonways instead of horses. Charles Brandling of Gosforth House, Newcastle upon Tyne, leads the way; John Blenkinsop, their agent at Middleton Leeds, employs Mathew Murray to construct a locomotive for his rack & pinion railway. Murray pays Trevithick patent royalties.

1812   George Stephenson is employed with a salary as enginewright to the Grand Allies.

1813   September: Murray's locomotive runs on Brandling's Kenton & Coxlodge rack & pinion railway near Newcastle; Robert's uncle and namesake is the *Engineman*.

1814   25 July: the first Stephenson locomotive *Blucher*, which closely follows Murray's design, runs on a smooth cast iron railway. Ralph Dodds, viewer; Nicholas Wood, under-viewer; and George Stephenson, enginewright are all part of the Killingworth construction team. Young Robert is also present.

1815   August: Robert attends Percy Street Academy, Newcastle upon Tyne and becomes a reading member of the Literary & Philosophical Society.

•   A prize of £1000 is offered for a practical miner's safety lamp.
     October to December: the *Geordie* safety lamp is made, tested and presented to the public. Together with Nicholas Wood, Robert is involved with the lamp's production. Sir Humphrey Davy also designs a lamp at the same time.

1816   July: Robert does the calculations for a sundial and during the next month helps his father to make the sundial, which is placed over their front door.

•   August: Robert gives his sundial drawing to William Losh, chemist and iron founder.

•   30 September: Losh and Stephenson's Patent 4067, which includes improvements to rails, wheels and steam springs for a six wheel locomotive.

1817   Robert begins to write letters for his father's signature during a heated row provoked by Sir Humphrey Davy. *A newspaper war was waged, in which the advocates of Stephenson were altogether victorious.*

1819   July: Robert leaves school to become an apprentice to Nicholas Wood at the Killingworth Collieries, in order to be qualified as a mining engineer.

•   George Stephenson accepts a contract to construct a railway for the Hetton Coal Company. Robert also *assisted in superintending the works of the Hetton Railway*.

1821   George and Nicholas Wood travel to Darlington to visit Edward Pease, leading Director of the Stockton & Darlington Railway Company. (S&DR) Subsequently George Stephenson accepts the position as engineer.

•   Robert abandons his training as a mining engineer in order to help with the Stockton & Darlington Railway (S&DR) survey. His father insists that the name *Robert Stephenson* is placed on the S&DR plans, reports and contracts as *Engineer*.

•   Robert in charge of the engine workshop at West Moor, Killingworth. He employs William Hutchinson as his chief mechanic.

•   June: William James, a land agent, surveyor and coal-master visits Killingworth. For twenty years this far-sighted man has advocated a railway network specifically for passengers and wishes to purchase locomotives capable of travelling at speed.

•   Robert modifies the 1816 patent engine and builds a high pressure four wheel locomotive, thus reducing the weight; this showpiece is described in August by William Stobart as *the latest and the best* of the Stephenson locomotives.

- October: Robert begins to construct the locomotives for the Hetton Railway.

1822 April: S&DR contractors are instructed to report to Robert at the West Moor engine workshop despite the fact that he is not employed at the colliery anymore. This indicates his presence and that he was still constructing the Hetton locomotives.

- August / September: helps William James with the first Liverpool to Manchester Railway (L&MR) survey. As this railway is intended primarily for passengers, Robert advises his mentor not to have a *fixed* engine and to *lay a strong railway and enjoy the advantage of Locomotive Engines*; in contrast to his father's objectives.
- October: *LOCOMOTIVE ENGINE 'DARLINGTON'* on the drawing board.
- Late October: Robert enrols as a student at Edinburgh University.

1823 Late April: completes one session as a student and then makes his first public appearance before a Parliamentary subcommittee for the second S & DR Bill.

Laying the foundations of an establishment for me: Robert Stephenson

- 23 June: at nineteen years old becomes the manager partner of a Company named after him 'Robert Stephenson & Co.' (RS&Co) There are five equal shareholders, Robert and George Stephenson; the Quaker cousins Edward Pease and Thomas Richardson and Michael Longridge, manager of the Bedlington Iron Works. The first *Engine Works*, established with the intention of specialising in locomotive construction, is situated in the cul-de-sac South Street and set in a rapidly developing area around Forth Street.

[now immediately behind Newcastle Central Station] Offices built c.1850 and boiler/plate workshop still survive.

- Robert has *to supervise the building operations, engage men, take orders, advise on contracts, draw plans, make estimates, keep the accounts, and in all matters, great or small, govern the young establishment on his own responsibility.* Later he earns the respectful title of *Chief.* At the adjacent Burrell Iron Works, he can also keep an eye on the construction of the S&DR Gaunless Bridge, the first iron railway structure.
- December: the factory is fully operational; new employees include the eighteen year old mining engineer Joseph Locke and the apprentice Thomas Gooch.

1824 Early February: Robert goes to London to attend Parliament for 34 non-consecutive days on the third S&DR Bill. During a gap between sessions he accompanies his uncle Robert to Cornwall in order to help complile a report on mining practice for a South American project to open up colonial Spanish silver and gold mines. Thomas Richardson is involved in this concern and hopes to gain steam engine orders for RS & Co.

- Early April: his father then takes over to secure a successful outcome for the S&DR Hagger Leazes branch line and Robert returns to Newcastle, friends are concerned for his health. Overburdened with work, a relaxing sea voyage is recommended as a possible cure.
- Late April: back in London, Robert signs a three-year contract with Herring, Graham & Powles, agents for what becomes the Colombian Mining Association. He completes the engine designs for RS & Co. orders.

- 4 June: Robert, an at once dutiful and determined son, writes of a wish to help his father on the *undertaking at Liverpool but I do not even now despair of taking the Chief part of his engagements on myself in a year or two.*
- 18 June: sails to South America on board the *Sir William Congreve* .
- 23 July: lands in La Guayra, does engineering and mineral surveillance work. Robert enjoys the magnificent Colombian scenery from his base at Santa Ana and the challenge of extracting silver from the mines. For the next three years, he is able to continue his education, receiving lessons in mathematics and natural science from Dr. Roullin; chemistry and geology from M. Boussingault.
- August: the experienced steam engine mechanic James Kennedy, replaces Robert as working manager of RS & Co., and completes the first three S&DR locomotives.
- December: 'George Stephenson & Son' (GS&Son) is founded with the same partners as RS & Co. In his absence, Robert is named as chief engineer, dividing a salary of £1500 per annum with his father. The firm occupies an adjoining office in South Street and is intended to provide an integrated service for prospective railway companies from surveying to completion. William James has been declared bankrupt and George Stephenson takes over most of his railway projects.

1825 March: George Stephenson is in the witness box for the Liverpool & Manchester Bill. He exaggerates the number of locomotives built under his auspices; the 'levels' taken by GS & Son apprentices are exposed as substantially flawed.

- 15 December: Robert writes to Michael Longridge about the *failure of the Liverpool and Manchester Bill… It is to be regretted that my father placed the conducting of the levelling under the care of young men without experience.* In turn Longridge expresses his concern: *Robert! my faith in engineers is wonderfully shaken. I hope when you return to us your accuracy will redeem their character.*

What I might do in England is known to myself only: Robert Stephenson.

1826 24 March: under pressure to stay in Colombia, Robert continues to explain how his prospects are with RS & Co. that he must receive the consent of his partners and states *my father must have suffered severely from my absence.*

- 5 May: the Liverpool & Manchester Railway (L&MR) Act receives the Royal Assent.
- 3 July: George Stephenson is appointed Engineer-in-Chief, with Joseph Locke and Charles Blacker Vignoles, the author of the successful survey, as Assistant Engineers.

1827 February: Locke writes to his friend in exile *that shade which was unfortunately cast on the fame of your father has disappeared.* But at the same time Robert receives a letter from George concerning the intended use of stationary engines placed on inclines along the L&MR. *I want these engines to be constantly moveing* [sic] *with an endless Rope so that the locomotive engines take hold of the Rope and go on with out stoping… my new plan of locomotive will be a huge job… you will think I have some mistaken ideas about this but I think not.*

- 16 July: Robert writes to Michael Longridge *The period of my departure from this place has at last really and truly arrived... I received a letter from Mr Richardson, in which he states that the factory was far from being in a good condition, and that unless I returned promptly to England it would not improbably be abandoned.*
- Meets Richard Trevithick in Carthegena: *Robert Stephenson was well inclined to listen to what were then considered to be visionary schemes.*
- Robert returns via New York: he wishes to see the *finest steam-boats in the world*. The steam engine pioneer John Stevens had introduced a multitubular boiler on steam-boats. His *Phoenix* of 1809 *became the first sea-going steam ship in the world.* Members of the Stevens family become associated with Robert throughout his life.
- *A few hours from port* his brig the *Bunker's Hill* is shipwrecked. All passengers and crew are saved but most of the cargo is lost.
- 21 September: Robert joins the fraternity of Freemasons in New York.
- Travels inland via river, lake and road to the Niagara Falls and Montreal.
- November: arrives back in Liverpool on the first-class packet ship, the *Pacific*, then travels to London and the continent.

1828   1 January: with renewed determination Robert Stephenson persuades his father to abandon indirect drive and writes of *endeavouring to reduce the size and ugliness of our travelling engines, by applying the engine* [cylinders] *either on the side of the boiler or beneath it entirely.* Beginning his locomotive development programme with *Lancashire Witch* and *America*, he aims to simplify the design and increase the boiler surface according to the ideas passed on to him by Richard Trevithick and John Stevens. *The great and immediate work* for the next five years is being in charge of his locomotive factory at Newcastle. But as the GS & Son joint engineer, railways also occupy him particularly *assisting his father with the Liverpool & Manchester.*

- June: travels to the continent in connection with a locomotive order for Marc Seguin. Then takes over the almost completed Canterbury & Whitstable Railway (C&WR), originated by William James; during the next month Robert also surveys the Kenyon & Leigh Junction Railway (K&LJR) and the Warrington & Newton Railway (W&NR)

Rely upon it, locomotives shall not be cowardly given up. I will fight for them until the last. They are worthy of a conflict: Robert Stephenson.

1829   March: Robert and Joseph Locke write their pro-locomotive Report because a deputation has recommended the use of stationary engines instead of locomotives to the L&MR Directors.

- April: the Stephenson & Locke Report is submitted to the Liverpool & Manchester Railway Directors, resulting in a decision to hold an open locomotive trial to take place at Rainhill in October with a prize of £500. George Stephenson and Henry Booth are to pay for Robert's *Premium Engine* entry.
- May: Robert takes a lease on 5 Greenfield Place, Summerhill Square, Newcastle upon Tyne and begins to design his entry soon to be called the *Rocket*.
- 17 June: marries Frances Sanderson in London.

- Summer: construction of the *Rocket* begins. Robert's technicians include William Hutchinson his chief mechanic since 1821 and draughtsman George Phipps, who draws the completed design on the *Chief's* office floor. Time is limited for any two-way correspondence. Robert writes obligation letters to Booth concerning their progress. To these queries, the only known written reply is from Locke. Neither owner visits RS & Co., despite a request for their presence at the *Rocket's* trial run.
- 21 August: although the firebox design is in Robert's hand, it has been built in Liverpool. He criticises the *neglect in workmanship* and notes *it is not square built.*
- September: the *Rocket* is reassembled at West Moor and tried on the private Killingworth Waggonway; then transported by land and sea to Liverpool.
- 6 and 8 October: the *Rocket* succeeds in completing the trial runs and fulfils all the conditions. Being aware of all possible mechanical problems, Robert Stephenson almost certainly directs these trials from the footplate, helped perhaps by Ralph Hutchinson. Between the official runs and after *Rocket*'s triumph, father George shows off the locomotive's prowess in typical fashion giving spectators joyrides. Even with flexible arrangements, the other locomotive entries fail to complete the course.
- The prize money is shared by Robert and the two owners.

The trials at Rainhill have set people railway mad…We are getting rapidly on with four locomotive engines for Liverpool, which I am confident will exceed the Rocket in powers…

1830 Robert goes on to explain how one locomotive would leave RS & Co. about New Year's Day and the rest a few weeks later. More locomotives follow; Robert's schematic drawings January 1828 - June 1830 show how he achieved his goal. Stage by stage, he evolves a compact, powerful and reliable locomotive. The *Rocket* was pivotal to his scheme. His formula did not break down upon the introduction of new ideas.
- Ordered in April and on the drawing board by June, the *Northumbrian* becomes the forerunner of all outside cylinder locomotives.
- April: becomes a Member of the Institution of Civil Engineers.
- 3 May: *The opening of the Canterbury Railway went off remarkably well, without a single mishap.* This is the first railway to have scheduled passenger trains, hauled by Robert Stephenson's locomotive, the *Invicta*.
- 14 May: both the K&LJR and W&NR are incorporated. Followed by the Leicester & Swannington on 29 May and Robert is appointed Engineer-in-Chief. Attending to these railways are considered as *trifles,* but initially an Engineer-in-Chief had to be a *Manager* as well. Running railways under his control gave him an opportunity to secure locomotive orders and also appreciate operational problems arising, thus altering his locomotive designs accordingly.

My courage at times almost fails me and I fear that some fine morning my reputation may break under me like an egg-shell:
Robert Stephenson

Like most creative people, Robert lived on a knife-edge: doubts and questions led to positive answers. He did not crack under the pressure.

- Ordered on 21 June and sent to Liverpool on 3 September, the *Planet* is to become the prototype for inside cylinder locomotives. But at this time, Robert lacks support from his father and also some members of the L&MR Board, because of very real *fears of broken crank axles.*
- 20 October: as joint chief engineer to GS & Son, Robert does the preliminary survey of the London to Birmingham railway (L&BR) but he advises the company not to submit the Bill to Parliament at the next session, due to the limited time and the need to *improve many important points for revision.* He also refuses to be involved with the railway link between Birmingham and Warrington, later called the Grand Junction (GJR). *It is adverse to my feelings to be concerned with any undertaking which might interfere with Mr Locke's views as his kindness to my father has been very great.*
- November: Robert L. Stevens orders a 'Planet' type locomotive with a modified firebox, for the Camden & Amboy Railway (C&AR) USA.

1831 Stevens' *John Bull* is despatched in June 1831 to the C&AR, followed by three more locomotives for the Mohawk & Hudson Railway, USA.
- While surveying a railway to connect collieries around Swannington to Leicester, Robert appreciates the possibility of a vast coal seam. He *strongly urges his father* to purchase Snibston Estate situated on top of the coalfield. In turn George persuades two of his Liverpool friends to join him in this very lucrative enterprise.
- 27 June: RS & Co. partners agree that Robert could be a partner with Charles Tayleur to establish a locomotive factory at Newton-le-Willows. [Vulcan Foundry]

- Late Autumn: Robert surveys the second L&BR line.

1832 February: the L&BR Bill is read for the first time; passed by the House of Commons, then rejected by the House of Lords. Lord Wharncliffe gave Robert encouragement, *my young friend don't take this to heart. The decision is against you: but you have made such a display of power that your fortune is made for life.*
- September: Robert personally orders a three axle 'Planet' type. This 2-2-2 locomotive is later called *Patentee.*
- He is appointed Consultant Engineer to Stanhope & Tyne Railway (S&TR).
- Late Autumn: conducts the third survey for another L&BR Bill.

1833 16 January: Robert designs the *Davy Crockett* with a bogie, a component which enables locomotives to adjust to the sharp curves of railways in the USA.
- 6 May: the London & Birmingham and the Grand Junction railways are incorporated.
  John Rastrick reports on Robert's plans to the L&BR: *Let nothing deter you from executing the work… on the most scientific principles.*
- 28 May: Robert receives a letter from the L&BR reassuring him *as to the appointment of engineer… you may be easy on that head.*
- July & August: Robert goes to the continent to secure locomotive orders.
- 20 September: signs the contract with the L&BR directors as Engineer-in-Chief.
- 7 October: obtains a patent; Robert Stephenson's Specification 6484. The variations are a six-wheel 'Planet' type. All his former practices are incorporated into this enlarged locomotive called

generally the 'Patentee', such as the multitubular boiler with integral firebox, smokebox, blast pipe to stimulate the fire, steel leaf springs and his latest invention: the steam brake. He is recognised as the leader of his technological age, providing a locomotive prototype for both sides of the Atlantic.

- Robert receives *instructions to stake out the line* [L&BR] *without delay.*
- Robert Stephenson becomes renowned as *the most successful civil engineer of his time,* it is with great regret that he leaves Greenfield Place, Newcastle upon Tyne. To the management of RS & Co., *he devoted himself as a labour of love, thinking over improvements and designing innovations, the necessity for which had become apparent in the working of his lines of railways.*
- Frances and Robert Stephenson move to St. Mary's Cottage, Hampstead and then to a comfortable house at Haverstock Hill, London.
- 9 November: RS & Co. records *A List of Drawings of a 60 Horse Patent Locomotive sent to Messrs. Tayleur & Co., Vulcan Foundry, by Mr Stephenson's directions.*
- 12 November: a 20 horsepower high pressure stationary engine is ordered from RS & Co. for Messrs. Tayleur & Stephenson to power their new factory.

1834   ***Robert Stephenson almost lived on the line…*** The scale of the 111 mile long railway from London to Birmingham was unprecedented. Due to the accuracy of his designs and attention to detail, his ability to organise and choose capable subordinates, he gains their respect and can delegate mundane day-to-day activities. The works were completed on time at a cost of £5,500,000. Robert's

Diary reads:
11 February: *At Kilburn office writing specification and sketching bridges.*
15 May: *At St John's Wood all-day writing letters and designing bridges…*

1835   May: Robert accompanies his father to Brussels as a railway consultant.

- 3 July: the second L&BR Act authorises a 1½ mile extension. As the new resident engineer, Charles Fox exaggerates the extent of innovative work done while holding this position, such as perfecting the skew bridge, previously introduced by others; credit for the concept and detailing of the tied arch over the Regent Canal and the wrought iron train shed roof at Euston Station. Other engineers and an historian confirm that Robert's design of a tied arch was first introduced at Long Buckby in 1834 and completed before the L&BR extension; the same design of train shed roof as at Euston had been preceded by that of Curzon Street station built as planned in 1833/4. Roscoe calls Robert's structures *conceptions of the master mind.*
- 31 August: Great Western Railway incorporated; I.K Brunel Engineer-in-Chief. *Brunel borrowed Robert Stephenson's plans and uses them as the best possible system of draughting. His efficient methods became recognised models for railway practice.* This practice also enabled Robert to be in charge of many projects at once.

1836   Great Britain is experiencing an outbreak of wild financial speculation, many railways are projected and Robert opens an office at 16 Duke Street London in February.

- 12 April: Robert defends his frequent absences from RS & Co. *I am satisfied if it had not been for exertions made away from home, the Establishment would scarcely have been in existence at this moment. I cannot therefore avoid feeling hurt...*

- As joint chief engineer to GS & Son, the construction of the Birmingham & Derby Junction, York & North Midland and North Midland begin under his direction.
- November: RS & Co. receives six Patentee-type locomotive orders from the Grand Junction Railway. They are despatched in the spring of 1837.

1837   20 February: Robert moves his London office to 35½ Great George Street, London.

- June: first use of the Electric Telegraph is on the L&BR. Although used initially for business messages, it was soon established on the London & Blackwall Railway for signalling train movements. This enables faster and safer journeys and increases the railway's capacity. Robert and his employees continued to promote its use.
- GS & Son suffers its first major setback. Robert's proposed route from London to Brighton is rejected. He defends his plans, sections and designs in a pamphlet. The elder Stephenson's statements had cast a cloud. Counsel: *Your name was put to it as principal engineer and you signed the estimate ... the father should not put his name upon the credit of the son unless he has done the work.* George Stephenson replied: *I have brought him up since a child... and I ought to have some benefit.*
- 4 July: the Grand Junction (GJR), the world's first long distance railway, is opened on time and within the bounds of the estimated costs; Joseph Locke, Engineer-in-Chief.
- 23 December: the L&BR celebration dinner is held at Dunchurch, Warwickshire. On a presentation silver

tureen is the inscription: *to Robert Stephenson, Esq, Engineer-in-Chief of the London and Birmingham Railway, a tribute of the respect and esteem from the members of the Engineering Department who were employed under him in the execution of that great work. Presented on the eve of their gradual separation.*

1838   4 June: a 22 mile section of the Great Western Railway is opened from Paddington to Maidenhead operated by two Robert Stephenson Patentee-type locomotives the *Morning Star* and *North Star*. Brunel wrote: *We have a splendid engine of Stephenson's it would be a beatyfull* [sic] *ornament in the most elegant drawing room.*

- 24 June: opening of the L&BR throughout. A celebratory dinner is held at Dees Royal Hotel, Birmingham. The historian Thomas Roscoe publishes a book to celebrate the railway; *Assuredly the name of Robert Stephenson will, in after years, be recorded as one of the greatest men of the age in which he lived.*
- 28 June: opening of the Victoria Viaduct crossing the River Wear, a few mile east of Durham; it will form a vital link in the first East Coast route to London. *This beautiful bridge with elegant curves of massive stone... will probably exist as a memorial to Robert Stephenson's capacity.* The structure holds the record as having the largest railway masonry arch in England.

1839   April: Robert spends about three months on the continent. He visits France, Switzerland and then Italy as a railway consultant.

- 2 July: *gives evidence before the Select Committee on Railways.*
- 16 July: *at Derby concerning the railway station.*

- 18 July: *viewing the Sheffield & Rotherham Railway works,* which had been opened 31 October 1838, with a further section completed on 10 August 1839.
- John Stephenson, the leading railway contractor, establishes a testimonial committee for Robert. The York and North Midland; Midland Counties; Birmingham & Derby Junction; are all completed during the summer. The London & Blackwall; Manchester & Birmingham; Manchester & Leeds; Sheffield & Rotherham and a section of the Northern & Eastern railways are due to be completed during the following year. Over £1250 is collected; and a service of plate with a candelabrum are presented to Robert Stephenson at a dinner held in his honour at the Albion Hotel, Aldersgate, London on 16 November.

1840   The Stanhope & Tyne (S&TR) fiasco: unfortunately in lieu of his fee as a consultant engineer Robert accepted substantial shares in 1832, consequently he is responsible for an accumulated large debt. George Hudson, the 'Railway King' comes on the scene and reorganises a previously arranged scheme to relieve this situation by an amalgamation and incorporation. Five miles of the S&TR will link the Durham Junction and Brandling Junction as part of a passenger railway serving Gateshead, South Shields and Sunderland, thus making the S&TR financially viable. This link will be part of the proposed East Coast railway from London to Edinburgh. Hudson forms a pact with the projectors of the Newcastle and Darlington Junction line; the Great North of England Railway (GNER) is part of the plan.

1841   George Hudson appointed Chairman of the Newcastle and Darlington Junction Company and succeeds by rapidly welding the east coast link.
- 3 January: an attempt to open the southern section of the GNER, but problems with the bridges and earthworks occur. So Robert Stephenson takes over as Engineer-in-Chief from his cousin by marriage, Thomas Storey. Using this position, Robert also becomes Engineer-in-Chief designate to N&DJR.
- An economic slump in Great Britain begins to affect locomotive production.
- 23 June: obtains a patent; Robert Stephenson's Specification 8998, the 'Long-boiler' type locomotive, the intention being to improve heat efficiency; his 'working gear' is the last stage before the 'Stephenson Link Motion'. Within months, while visiting Derby, Robert revealed: *there is no occasion to try any further at scheming valve motions; one of our people has now hit upon a plan that beats all the other valve motions.* No patent is taken out for the 'StephensonLink Motion'.
- 30 June: Great Western Railway opens, vastly over budget, from Paddington to Bristol.
- November: due to difficulties in raising capital, Robert Stephenson agrees with the North Midland Railway shareholders to halve the fees due to him for general management of the railway and to be retained as locomotive superintendent, again with his salary halved.

1842   18 June: the Newcastle & Darlington Junction Railway (N&DJR) is incorporated.
- September: as a consultant to the South Eastern Railway, one of Robert's tasks is to report on *French Railways.* His office is still 35½ Great George Street.

- 4 October: his wife Frances dies and he moves to 15 Cambridge Square, London.
- 4 November: Robert writes to Edward Pease regarding *the dissolution of partnership with Michael Longridge*.

1843 June: Robert's London office now at 24 Great George Street.
- Summer: in Italy and Germany as a railway consultant, *protecting the interest of the Newcastle factory* and *securing new and powerful connections wherever he went.*
- 20 September: as *Engineer of the N&DJR* Robert is to be approached in connection with the design of the railway structure to cross the Tyne in order that the *Details may be arranged to the satisfaction of guaranteeing Companies.*

1844 9 April: completes his Report for the Chester & Holyhead Railway (C&HR) on the atmospheric system operating in Ireland and condemns it, *the perfect operation of the whole is dependent on each individual part*. The failure of just one link in the *complicated series of machinery* could bring the railway to a standstill and cause delays to the *great chain of public lines*. Robert still recommends the locomotive's flexibility, whatever merits the atmospheric system may appear to have. Championed by I. K. Brunel, the atmospheric system was introduced on the South Devon Railway. The company paid dearly for Brunel's failed costly experiment.
- June: Robert gives £1,000 to the *Industrial Exhibition* Committee.
- 18 June: on *Waterloo* day the N&DJR is opened. A dinner is held at the Assembly Rooms, Newcastle upon Tyne to celebrate a continuous line of railway from the Thames to the Tyne, virtually built under Stephenson auspices.
- 4 July: C&HR is incorporated; Robert appointed Engineer-in-Chief.
- November: Robert's plans submitted for the Newcastle & Berwick Railway Bill.
- I.K. Brunel proposes an alternative inland route between Newcastle and Berwick to be powered by the atmospheric system.

1845 Britain enjoys an economic boom. Some railway shares are yielding 10% dividends. The 'Railway Mania' results in an excessive amount of time spent in Parliament by leading engineers. Between 1845-8 Robert stands as a witness both for and against 60 Bills. The untimely deaths of *Stephenson, Brunel, Locke and Errington* are later attributed to the long hours spent in overcrowded committee rooms, without regular meals *nervous systems became unstrong… stomach, brain and liver were alike irretrievably injured. Robert Stephenson might naturally have looked forward to many more years of quiet authority.*
- Robert takes over from Sir John Macneill as Engineer-in-Chief to the Londonderry & Enniskillen Railway and saves over £209,000 for the company.
- 13 & 14 March: drawings for an anticipated tubular girder to bridge the Menai Straits and River Conway (C&HR) are prepared under Robert's direction. *The calculations followed the principle previously adopted by Eaton Hodgkinson in determining an empirical formula for cast iron girders*. John Laird was on the C&HR Board and as Robert put it *expressed his confidence in the great strength which such a structure as I proposed would possess.*

But George Stephenson *at first experienced some doubts*; on the very day that he was given an explanation on the tubular principle, his long-term friend William Fairbairn opportunely visits the Stephenson office. That Fairbairn gave his approval undoubtedly helped to convince the sceptic; that the experiments were to be conducted at his Millwall shipyard would also reassure.

- April: witnesses appear before House of Commons Select Committee appointed to investigate the atmospheric system. Among others I.K. Brunel, William Cubitt and C.B.Vignoles give their support; Robert Stephenson, Joseph Locke and Robert Nicholson testify against it. Time proved the system to be a technical failure.

- 5 May: Robert proposes a tubular bridge to form a *continuous* beam at the C&HR Bill proceedings, expressing *an unequivocal opinion as to the sufficiency of the tube alone*.

- 30 June: the second C&HR Act is incorporated for the five miles to cross the Menai Straits and its approaches. Robert stated; *I now commenced an experimental investigation on tubular constructions and availed myself of all the practical and scientific aid which might be within my reach*. Soon the eminent mathematician Eaton Hodgkinson will be employed to assist with the project for the two box-girder bridges, the Britannia at the Menai Straits with the two spans of 460 ft. and two of 230 ft. and a single span of 400 ft. to cross the river at Conway.

- 31 July: Newcastle & Berwick Railway Act incorporated. Robert Stephenson is appointed Engineer-in-Chief with responsibility for all structures under and over this railway, including the Dean Street viaduct, the High Level Bridge, Newcastle Central Station and the Royal Border Bridge.

- 6 August: Robert is the first to give evidence before the Gauge Commissioners. It is their task to *examine the safety, accommodation, speed and economy* between the Stephenson 4' 8½" and the Brunel 7' 0¼" broad gauge. The day of reckoning arrived when the two gauges met, causing disruption to the system. As a locomotive designer, Robert conceded that initially a 5' gauge would have been desirable; he explained how recently *the working gear has been much simplified... we have ample space*. Joseph Locke also admitted that he would *have adopted a gauge rather wider than the narrow gauge, but certainly not so wide as 7 feet*. The Commissioners found in favour of the narrow gauge of 4' 8½" which eventually became standard.

- 21 August: Edward Pease writes in his Diary - *went to Newcastle with cousin T.Richardson to settle our co-partnership with George and Robert Stephenson, when it was agreed that W.Hutchinson should come in as a fifth...*

1846   19 January: Edward Pease continues to record in his Diary, *to Newcastle to settle a new deed of partnership for twenty-one years with Robert Stephenson*.

- March: Robert appoints Edwin Clark to supervise and report back to him on the tubular girder experiments. At the same time, Fairbairn had become dissatisfied with Hodgkinson's abstract scientific approach, but Robert valued his experimental work done since the previous September, and retains him.

- 4 March: Sir Robert Peel speaks in the House of Commons supporting 'undulating railways'. Robert writes a

- 10 April: Britannia Bridge foundation stone laid by Frank Forster (resident engineer) Robert Stephenson had engaged the architect Francis Thompson to help prepare *the designs for the masonry, and he was both instructed to complete his drawings for the foundations to establish the quantity of masonry and prepare the plans & specifications to lay before the contractors.*
- 12 June: Conway Bridge foundation stone laid by Alexander Ross (resident engineer)
- 24 June: William James's Testimonial as the founder of the passenger railway network; the first two names on the committee are Robert Stephenson and Joseph Locke.
- 16 July: Robert is joint Engineer-in-Chief with Joseph Locke of the London & North Western Railway (L&NWR), it is an amalgamation of their previous railways from London to Carlisle and branch lines. Robert Dockray is a resident engineer and offers remarkable insights in his daily Diary: regarding the Britannia Bridge, he expresses a wish to do *all I can to   assist in building up the reputation of my great Chief Robert Stephenson and especially in this case when an attempt is being made to rob him of the credit due for the successful realisation of this grand undertaking.*

1847   3 March: Robert gives his approval to Edwin Clark's suggestion of a single row of top cells to strengthen the tube, thus finalising the design. The C&HR directors have become aware that William Fairbairn has re-assigned a contract to gain personal profit without their consent. There is a conflict of interest.

24 May: a trussed girder bridge, spanning the River Dee on the C&HR collapses, killing five people; *although designed by an assistant who was famous for his powers of calculation, it is unaccountable that the practical eye of Mr Stephenson should have been for the moment blind…Locke came down to Chester on the occasion of the inquest a month later to give his support.* The court recommends a Royal Commission on the *Application of Iron to Railway Structures.* (AIRS)

- 7 July: on behalf of L&NWR, Robert replies to a report by Brunel: *The Break of Gauge cannot be remedied by the mixture of gauges* and stresses the need for *uniformity* and *simplicity of construction and arrangement, which can also ensure the economy, safety and efficiency of the railway system.*
- 30 July: Robert elected as a Tory MP for Whitby without opposition.
- Autumn: visits Norway with G.P. Bidder, his assistant, and is consulted about a railway.
- Moves home to 34 Gloucester Square, London.

1848   6 March: first Conway tube floated. Two days later on Wednesday 8 March, the *Manchester Guardian* reports the event: *Amongst the parties present were Mr Robert Stephenson the engineer of the railway* but the report fails to mention Fairbairn. On 15 March the omission is reported giving totally exaggerated claims *the floating and the raising of the tube have been carried on under the superintendence of Mr Fairbairn of this town.* A letter to the Editor from G. P. Bidder is then published on the 22 March, denying the claim stating that Robert was *entirely responsible, not only for the designing of the structure, but also for all the arrangements connected with its removal… The company looked to Mr Robert Stephenson alone as their engineer.* The Editor in turn apologised for giving a false impression.

- 16 March: Robert gives evidence to the AIRS commissioners; he confirms having had *a great number of experiments made at Newcastle during the time of the High Level Bridge's erection...I cannot use his* [Eaton Hodgkinson] *formulae always and I should be sorry to be tied down to them.* He emphatically did not wish to be restricted to *Rules* and *Legislation.* Joseph Locke confirmed that riveting wrought iron plates in order to create load bearing beams as locomotive frames *have been used very long*; indeed were introduced by Robert in 1830 on the *Northumbrian* to support outside cylinders, then developed by Locke and his teams at Crewe and Sotteville, Rouen. Having made boilers by riveting wrought iron plates since 1821, did Robert consider the tubular girder as an extension of a mechanical process? His contemporary colleagues unequivocally acknowledged the significance of the tubular girder project: *To the genius which designed and executed the Britannia and Conway Bridges on the tubular principle, at a time when the use of wrought iron for large beams, was nearly unknown, the engineering world is indebted for important and profound investigations into the properties of wrought iron beams.*
- 16 April: the first Conway tube is raised to its final position and two days later Robert drives the first locomotive through the tube.
- 22 May: Fairbairn finally hands in his resignation to the C&HR.
- 12 August, father George Stephenson dies suddenly at Tapton House.
- 17 August: Edward Pease writes in his Diary *went in the forenoon to Tapton House, late G. Stephenson's residence and received from Robert a welcome reception; had a serious friendly conference with him, under a feeling expressed to him of my belief that it was a kindness to him his father was taken... the attendance of his funeral appeared to me to be a right step due to my association with him and his son. I do not feel condemned in so doing...*
- 18 September: Robert accepts the presidency of Institution of Mechanical Engineers which he held for four years.

1849   20 February: resulting from an inquiry by an employee of the London Stock Exchange, George Hudson's railway financial activities are exposed as being highly dubious. A Committee of Inquiry *took the view that Mr Hudson standing in the relation of trustee to the company, had acted improperly in selling the shares at a profit.* Other committees of investigation were appointed in May 1849 and reported many instances of abusing the privileges of his position for personal gain; he had paid dividends out of capital. Hudson resigned immediately as Chairman to the York, Newcastle and Berwick (YN&BR) and North Midland Railway Companies. Hudson's downfall had adverse repercussions on the railway industry for a decade. Many associated with him were not immune from scrutiny, and all business activities associated with Hudson were affected, such as the large housing development at Whitby being curtailed. The planned ambitious portico for the NCS was almost certainly doomed; the architect associated with both projects was John Dobson.
- 7 June: Robert elected a Fellow of the Royal Society - *A distinction highly prized by men of science was conferred on the inventor of the Tubular Bridge.*

- 20 June: floating and positioning of the Britannia Bridge's first tube. Joseph Locke and I.K. Brunel are present to give Robert moral support.
- 28 September: the official opening of the High Level Bridge (HLB) by Queen Victoria. Spanning the river Tyne this was the first road and rail bridge in the world. The bow-string girder design had been introduced on the L&BR. *The earliest railway bridge on this plan was designed by Mr Robert Stephenson in 1834 and erected in 1835 at Weedon.* (Long Buckby, L&BR) The railway from Gateshead to Tweedmouth had been opened on 29 August 1848 using contemporary wooden structures; the new station roof at Newcastle and the Royal Border Bridge still had to be completed. For both structures he employed reliable assistant engineers to ensure that his *plans are carefully and strictly attended to.* Concerning this railway project, Thomas Harrison stated in a published letter; *The plans have been prepared under my direction: - the designs are not mine, but my friend Mr Robert Stephenson.* Even the contractors had to obey Robert's instructions implicitly. The HLB contract reads *No deviation from any of the provisions of this contract, Specification or drawing will be permitted unless with sanction in writing of the Company's Principal Engineer.*

1850 26 February: *the Gateshead Observer* reports the two box girders to span Half Moon Street and West Street, Gateshead are being manufactured at RS &Co.
- 5 March: together with others on the footplate Robert drives the first train through the continuous tube forming the first railway bridge to span the sea. He ceremoniously drives the last rivet into the Britannia Tubular Girder.

- 15 May: Robert writes to Edward Pease just before a tube is floated and fixed, *I am prevented having the pleasure of the visit to Darlington on the 22nd... I sincerely regret this... opportunity of saying publicly how much the wonderful progress of railways was dependent upon... the first great experiment and how much that issue was influenced by your great discernment and your confidence.*
- 15 June: Robert writes to Edward Pease: *The suggestion which your kind note contains is quite in accordance with my own feelings and intentions respecting retirement... I trust that your prayer for the Divine blessing to grant me happiness and quiet comfort will be fulfilled.*
- 19 June: Robert awarded Hon. M.A. from Durham University.
  Robert Stephenson believes his knowledge in chemistry to surpass his attainments in engineering.
- 30 July: to celebrate the completion of a continuous line of railway built under his direction from Euston, London to Berwick-upon-Tweed at a dinner held in Robert's honour on the Central Station's platform, Newcastle upon Tyne. Behind the high table are large illustrations of his achievements, notably and centrally placed, the Britannia Bridge. The occasion gives him an opportunity to both reflect, state how engineering practices have changed and praise Thomas Harrison his assistant engineer on the Gateshead to Tweedmouth line. *Beyond drawing the outline, he had no right to claim any credit for the works above where they now sat.*
- 9 August: member of Royal Yacht Squadron; his new yacht *Titania* will be a means of escape. *Ships have no knockers, happily.*

- 19 August: the Alnwick branch line is opened. A box girder, manufactured at RS & Co. crosses the Great North Road and another *large tubular bridge is to be erected* on the York & North Midland Railway over the river Aire at Brotherton. Later, Sir Edward Harland recalled that RS & Co. were making many marine engine boilers and had contracted to *build for the government three large iron caissons for the Keyham Docks,* which were *very similar in construction to an ordinary iron ship.*
- 29 August: Queen Victoria officially opens the Central Station and Royal Border Bridge. In the evening, the Engineer-in-Chief is a guest of honour at the Assembly Rooms Newcastle, *the mayor occupying the chair and Robert Stephenson sitting by his side.* He had just refused a knighthood. Punch comments *We are glad that he sent back the insulting offer when Lord Mayors are made baronets by the dozen.*
- September: Robert Stephenson attempts to retire. As *Chief* of his workforce, the *feudal sway* that he holds over his employees is over; they now became colleagues and use his offices at 24 Great George Street. The Berkeley brothers go to Bombay as chief resident engineers on the Great Indian Peninsular Railway. He travels to Switzerland and advises the new Federal Republic about a railway network; from Genoa he sails to Egypt in his yacht *Titania.* Said Pasha, Viceroy of Egypt, seeks his advice on a railway.

1851 March: Robert accepts the post of Engineer-in-Chief for the Alexandria to Cairo Railway: contracts are drawn up, but the line is slightly changed later.
- May: as a Commissioner of the Great Exhibition, Robert had ensured that Joseph Paxton's Crystal Palace design was accepted, but etiquette prevents the promotion of his own inventions and engineering achievements.
- 2 July: Robert's first tube over the river Aire at Brotherton is passed for traffic, but on 4 November, the second tube fails due to larger trains being run on the line. He authorises a modification to take place. During the next decade RS & Co. manufacturers 38 wrought iron bridges in the *Boiler / Plate Department.*
- July: with his yacht *Titania,* accepts the challenge of the American Commodore Stevens to race *America.* Thus began the America Cup challenges.
- Autumn: Robert goes to Norway as Engineer-in-Chief of the Christiania (Oslo) to Miosen Lake Railway, completed 1854 and is awarded the Cross of St.Olaff.

1853 27 April: Thomas Richardson dies at Great Ayton. Robert goes to the North East; on 13 May he arranges *Richardson's share… to… be transferred to Joseph Pease.*
- 21 June: *Titania II* launched.
- Robert submits his designs of the tubular girder bridge to cross the river St Lawrence, Canada. It will be the world's longest bridge.
- July-September: Robert goes to Canada. On 19 August, with his assistant engineer Alexander Ross, he is a guest at a banquet in Montreal. Robert's speech is considered to be *the best he had ever made in public…*
- 7 September: As a L&NWR resident engineer, R.B. Dockray visits Robert's brother-in-law and chief clerk, John Sanderson, at 24 Great George Street. *Talked over all my old acquaintances - very little change appears to have taken place in their position. They*

are scattered all over the world, the representatives of their master.

- October: John Sanderson dies. Robert suffers from severe depression; this is reflected in information given to Samuel Smiles for his father's biography. Closing his house at 34 Gloucester Place, Robert *took apartments in Thomas's hotel Berkeley Square and did not return to his residence till twelve months of mourning had expired.*

1854 3 July: nominated by Faraday, Robert becomes a member of the Royal Institution.
- Autumn: Robert spends over a month in the North East accompanying the author Samuel Smiles to familiar sites. On 24 September he writes of *spending some time in Whitby before I enter the Coally Tyne.*
- 23 October: Edward Pease writes in his Diary - *My friend Robert Stephenson the engineer, to spend two or three days with me - a man of most highly gifted and talented power of mind, of benevolent, liberal, kindly, just, generous dispositions, in company most interesting*; on the following day… *After breakfast, Robert Stephenson and four more went up the S&DR line as far as Hounds Gill [sic] and enjoyed their day.* Accompanied by Thomas Bouch, Robert in fact went to Hownes Gill to inspect the site of an intended viaduct as Consultant Engineer. Subsequently he drastically altered Bouch's intended delicate arch design. Due to anticipated problems with the foundations, Robert reduced the loading to half a ton per sq ft by adding recesses, inverted arches and splayed buttresses. Completed in 1858, this very graceful viaduct built of firebrick from Pease & Co. reaches a height of 150 ft and is 730 ft long.

1855 10 April: Robert confides with Thomas

Sopwith about having to go to the Paris Exhibition and *preside over the Civil Engineering Jury, having been requested to do so by the Royal Commission. I begged off needs must when the Devil drives.* He is made a Chevalier de la Légion d'Honneur by Napoleon III.
- 23 October: Robert writes to his friend Sopwith: *I sincerely condole with you… in my experience the severest is that of losing a kind and loving wife. When it fell upon me, I felt that even time could not soften the anguish but happily our mental as well as our physical constitution is wonderfully and fearfully made.* He goes on to reassure his friend that time does heal and new happiness is found.

1856 President of the Institution of Civil Engineers for a two-year term. During these years most of his time is spent in London. He lends his yacht to Professor Piazzi Smyth, the Astronomer Royal for Scotland, *who was sent with very limited means to Tenerife to make scientific observations.*
- Late autumn: with friends, Robert visits the Alexandria to Cairo Railway opened about nine months earlier and views his *ferry-bridge* at work. Sopwith wrote *of the excusable gratification which he experienced and the extreme interest and delight with which I viewed the great engineering work,* manufactured at RS & Co.

1857 Birth of his godson Robert Stephenson Smyth Powell (later Lord Baden-Powell)
- 24 June: receives a Doctorate of Civil Law from Oxford University.
- 1 October: extensive trip on *Titania II* around the coast of Great Britain.

1858 31 July: Edward Pease dies at Darlington.

- Robert visits Sunderland. *After receiving an address from the workmen then engaged in preserving that noble relic of Thomas Paine's genius for mechanics- the bridge over the Wear.* He replied *There are no members of society for whom I have a higher respect than for industrious and intelligent workmen. It is to them that the engineer is indebted for the full and efficient realisation of his conceptions.*
- 4 October: Michael Longridge dies at Bedlington.
- 14 October: in *Titania II*, Robert sails to Egypt.
- 25 December: dines with I.K. Brunel in Cairo.

1859   15 August: Robert sails to Norway accompanied by many colleagues.

- 3 September: he gives his last speech at a dinner held in his honour and is taken ill with jaundice. *Titania II* reaches Lowestoft on 13 September.
- 15 September: Isambard Kingdom Brunel dies of Bright's disease.
- 12 October: at his home 34 Gloucester Square, Robert Stephenson dies of *obstinate congestion of the liver followed by dropsy of the whole system.*
- Friday 21 October: buried centre nave of Westminster Abbey.
- Joseph Locke, President of Institution of Civil Engineers stated: *Robert Stephenson achieved some of the greatest works of art which have been witnessed in our day, he obtained at the same time an eminence in the scientific world rarely reached by any practical professional man.*

REFERENCES for the ENDNOTES

If a manuscript has been correctly transcribed in a publication, this reference is given for ease of access.

Abbreviations	Sources
CONDER	Conder, FR, *Personal Recollections of English Engineers, 1868,* Reprinted London,1983
DENDY	Dendy Marshall, CF, *A History of British Railways,* London, 1938
DPL	Document held in Darlington Public Library.
DOCKRAY	Robert Dockray's Diary, *Journal of Transport History,* first series, Vol.7, No.2
DRO	Document held in Durham County Record Office.
EN BRIT	Encyclopaedia Britannia, 8th Edition
ERH I	*Early Railway History,* Vol.I, a collection of documents held in NCL
ETHICS	Jarvis, Adrian, (ed.) *Nineteenth Century Business Ethics,* Liverpool,1992.
Ev.L&MR	Minutes of Evidence, Liverpool & Manchester Bill, House of Lords Committee, 1825
Ev.AIRS	Report of Commissioners: *The Application of Iron to Railway Structures* (1849)
EV.N&CR	Minutes of Evidence, Newcastle & Carlisle Railway, House of Commons Committee 1829
FRANCIS	Francis, John, *History of the English Railway,* 2 Vols, London, 1851
G.OBS.	*Gateshead Observer*
GROVE	Grove, CL., *The Life and Letters of Sir George Grove,* London, 1903
HLRO	Document held in the House of Lords Record Office.
ICE	Document held in the Institution of Civil Engineers Library.
ILN	*Illustrated London News,* 19 October 1850
IME	Document held in the Institution of Mechanical Engineers Library.
JEAF	Jeaffreson,JC, *The Life of Robert Stephenson* 2 Vols, London, 1864
LCL	Document held in Liverpool City Libraries.
NCL	Document held in Newcastle City Library.
N.CHRON	Newcastle Chronicle
N.SOC.	Newcomen Society Publication

NRO	Document held in Northumberland Record Office.
PAINE	Paine, EMS, *The two James and the two Stephensons,* London, 1861
PEASE	Pease,AE, *The Diaries of Edward Pease,* London, 1907
PERCE	Smith, D. (ed.), *Perceptions of Great Engineers, Fact & fantasy,* London, 1994.
PRO	Document held in National Archives, Kew.
Proc. ICE	Minutes of the Proceedings of the Institution of Civil Engineers.
ROLT	Rolt, LTC, *George and Robert Stephenson*, London, 1960
ROY. SOC.	Royal Society Proceedings, London Vol.10, 1859-60.
RS TRUST	Gazette, No 2 2004. Distributed privately.
ScM	Document held in the Science Museum, South Kensington.
SKEAT	SKEAT,WO, *George Stephenson ,his letters etc.* London, 1973
SMILES	Smiles, Samuel, *Lives of the Engineers* Vol.III, London, 1862
TREV	Trevithick, Francis, *Life of Richard Trevithick,* 2 Vols,London,1872
VULCAN	*Built by Stephenson,* written & published by English Electric Group, c1960
WARREN	Warren,JGH, *A Century of Locomotive Building by R Stephenson & Co,* Newcastle,1923
WOOD I	Wood, Nicholas, *Address,* to the Institute of Mining Engineers, February 1860.
WOOD II	Wood, Nicholas, *Notebook,* manuscript NRO.

ENDNOTES

TYNESIDE: the first nineteen years 1803-22

1.   JEAF   Vol.I p.2
2.   JEAF   Vol.I p.23
3.   JEAF   Vol.I p.28
4.   TREV   Vol.I p.186
5.   JEAF   Vol.I p.28
6.   TREV   Vol.II p.272
7.   SMILES   p.45
8.   JEAF   Vol.I p.16
9.   JEAF   Vol.I p.2
     SMILES   p.14
10. SMILES   p.48
11. SMILES   p.49
12. JEAF   Vol.I p.18
13. JEAF   Vol.I p.19
14. SMILES   p.59
15. JEAF   Vol.I p.55
16. JEAF   Vol.I p.30
17. JEAF   Vol.I p.21
18. JEAF   Vol.I p.8
19. WOOD I   p.34
20. SMILES   p.59
21. PERCE   p.56 Endnote 20
22. SMILES   p.60
23. JEAF   Vol.II p.184
24. TREV   Vol.I pp.193,194,207
25. WOOD I   pp..37-40
26. Burke's Peerage
     NRO 725/F.55
     SMILES   p.55
27. WARREN   p.19
     SMILES   pp.89-90
28. SMILES   p.94 Footnote
29. SMILES   p.91
30. SMILES   pp.94-5
31. PATENT 3431, 10.4.1811
32. SMILES   p.95
     PATENT 3700, 22.5.1813
33. Parish Registers, baptism of Robert's daughters
     Ann 1813 & Jane 1814
34. SMILES   pp.98-99
35. ETHICS   p.12 Footnote 46
     WOOD II   NRO 602/21
36. NRO 725/F.55 18.3.1815
37. JEAF   Vol.I p.43
38. SMILES   p.63
39. SMILES   p.114 Footnote
40. JEAF   Vol.I p.44
41. JEAF   Vol.I p.45
42. SMILES   p.107
43. WOOD   Address p.43
44. SMILES   p.109
45. WOOD II   NRO 602/21
46. WOOD I   p.44
47. SMILES   p.142
48. SMILES   p.127
49. JEAF   Vol.I p.39
50. FRANCIS   Vol.I p.197
51. JEAF   Vol.I p.33
52. SMILES   p.70
     JEAF   Vol.I p.44
53. PATENT   4067, 26.11.1816
     WARREN   p.28
     SMILES   p.139 Footnote
54. SMILES   p.139
55. G. OBS.   19 August 1848
     reporting speech 18.6.1844
56. WOOD I   p.55
     JEAF   Vol.I p.146
     SMILES   p.140
57. ROY SOC.   p.xxix
58. WARREN   p.28
59. JEAF   Vol.I p.48
60. SMILES   p.242
     WOOD I   p.56
61. N. CHRON   2 August 1850
62. SMILES   p.164 Footnote
63. WOOD I   p.53
64. Proc. ICE   Vol.31 p.203
65. WARREN   p.65
66. JEAF   Vol.I p.65
67. PEASE   p.85
68. JEAF   Vol.I p.53
69. SMILES   p.155 Footnote
     WOOD I   p.56
70. PEASE   p.87
71. PAINE   p.43
72. SMILES   pp.143-4
73. TREV   Vol.I p.198
74. SMILES   p.100
75. SKEATS   pp.46-9 NRO
76. WARREN   p.119
     Illusrations   p.25
77. WARREN   pp.97-8
78. SMILES   pp.162, 494
79. JEAF   Vol.I pp.54-5,243
     NCL   ERH I
     PRO   RAIL 667/278
     PRO   RAIL 667/274
80. JEAF   Vol.I p.54-5
81. SMILES   p.164 Footnote
     Circumstantial evidence strongly confirms
     the author to be the eighteen year old RS
     DENDY   p.150
82. PERCE   p.61 Endnotes 102-3
83. SKEATS   p.55
     LCL

84.	WARREN	p.144
85.	SMILES	p.103
86.	WARREN	pp.37,114 Illustrations

EDINBURGH & NEWCASTLE: 1822-4

1.	SMILES	p.144
2.	JEAF	Vol.I p.56
3.	SMILES	pp.146-7
4.	JEAF	Vol.I p.57
5.	ILN	p.309
6.	ROY. SOC.	p.xxix
7.	SKEATS	pp.59-60 LCL
8.	SKEATS	p.59 LCL
9.	JEAF	Vol.I p.55
	NCL	ERH I
	PRO	RAIL 667/278
	PRO	RAIL 667/274
10.	JEAF	Vol.I p.59
11.	GROVE	p.31-2
12.	The Times	21.9.1860
13.	JEAF	Vol.I p.68
14.	WARREN	p.65
15.	PEASE	p.265
16.	SMILES	pp.149-150
17.	DRO	D/Ho/C/63/5
18.	WARREN	p.52
	RS&Co. Minute Book. ScM	
19.	SMILES	p.249 Footnote
20.	ROY. SOC.	p.xxx
21.	JEAF	Vol.I p.66
22.	JEAF	Vol.I p.129, Vol.II p.162
	DOCKRAY	Diary 20.3.1850
23.	PAINE	p.68
24.	PAINE	pp.55-6
25.	JEAF	Vol.I pp.62-3
26.	JEAF	Vol.I pp.69-70 ICE
27.	IME	
28.	PAINE	p.59
29.	DRO	D/Sa/C/169
30.	PAINE	p.55
31.	JEAF	Vol.I p.73
32.	SKEATS	p.57 HLRO
33.	SKEATS	p.58 DPL
34.	JEAF	Vol.I p.70
35.	JEAF	Vol.I p.76 ScM
36.	JEAF	Vol.I p.68
37.	ROY. SOC.	p.xxix
	ILN	p.309
38.	N. SOC.	Vol.50 p.111
39.	PERCE	p.56 Endnote p.24
	EvN&CR	pp.126-7
40.	WARREN	p.54
	RS&Co. Min.Bk.ScM	
41.	WOOD I	p.52

42.	PERCE	p.56 Endnote 84
43.	JEAF	Vol.I p.72
44.	JEAF	Vol.I p.74-6

THE AMERICAS : 1824 - 7

1.	JEAF	Vol.I pp.80-1
2.	JEAF	Vol.I p.98
3.	WOOD I	p.34
4.	JEAF	Vol.I pp.91-2
5.	SMILES	p.478 Footnote
6.	JEAF	Vol.I p.67
7.	JEAF	Vol.I p.92
8.	ScM	MS 1151/5
9.	SMILES	pp.249-50 Footnote
10.	WARREN	p.162
11.	WARREN	p.68
12.	DRO	D/Ho/C/63/12
13.	WARREN	p.63
14.	WARREN	p.38-9
15.	WOOD I	p.61
16.	SMILES	p.143-4
17.	PERCE	p.60 Endnotes 89,90,92
18.	WARREN	p.119
19.	SKEATS	pp.102-4 LCL
20.	JEAF	Vol.I p.97

Stevens Institute of Technology
www.stevens-tech.edu/history/legl.htn
www.history.rochester.edu/system/stevens/hub.htm

21.	TREV	Vol.II p.272
22.	TREV	Vol.II pp.198-220
23.	Proc. ICE	Vol.19 p.177
24.	TREV	Vol.II p.273
25.	TREV	Vol.II pp.372-3
26.	WARREN	p.361
27.	ROY. SOC.	p.xxx
28.	JEAF	Vol.I p.105
29.	TREV	Vol.II p.274
30.	JEAF	Vol.I pp.105,191
	TREV	Vol.II pp.269,279
31.	TREV	Vol.II p.279
32.	JEAF	Vol.I p.109

NEWCASTLE upon TYNE: 1828-33

1.	JEAF	Vol.I p.114
2.	JEAF	Vol.I p.114-5
3.	WARREN	pp.145-7
4.	SMILES	p.139
5.	N. SOC	Vol.50 pp.25-36
	RS TRUST	pp.37-45

6.	WARREN	p.119
	PATENT 6484 & 8998	
	WARREN	pp.319-329,346-370
7.	Proc. ICE	Vol.31 p.203
8.	EN. BRIT	p.585
9.	JEAF	Vol.I p.132
10.	JEAF	Vol.I p.134
11.	JEAF	Vol.I p.153
12.	PERCE	p.58 Endnote 41
13.	WOOD I	pp.63-5
14.	PERCE	p.51 Endnote 51
15.	JEAF	Vol.I p.188
16.	ROY. SOC.	p.xxx
17.	JEAF	Vol.I p.116
18.	ETHICS	p.10 Endnote 31
19.	WARREN	p.111
20.	JEAF	Vol.I p.154
21.	WARREN	pp.140-3
	JEAF	Vol.I pp.119-121
22.	JEAF	Vol.I p.119
23.	SMILES	p.495
24.	WARREN	pp.148-9
25.	JEAF	Vol.I pp.121-2
26.	WARREN	pp.127-8
27.	PERCE	p.61 Endnote 108
28.	JEAF	Vol.I p.117
	WARREN	p.165
29.	WARREN	pp.166-170
	PERCE	p.62 Endnote 110
30.	JEAF	Vol.I p.133
31.	JEAF	Vol.I pp.123-4
32.	PERCE	pp.60;62;63
	Endnotes 87-9;116;137-140	
33.	ILN	p.309
34.	JEAF	Vol.I pp.124-5
35.	JEAF	Vol.I p.126
36.	JEAF	Vol.I p.134-6
37.	WARREN	p.228
	Illustrations	pp.211,214,216
38.	PERCE	p.61 Endnotes 97,98
	ICE.	T.Gooch Diary 1826
39.	JEAF	Vol.I p.136
40.	JEAF	Vol.I p.139
41.	PERCE	p.64 Endnotes 225-6
42.	Proc.ICE	Vol.XCVI (1889) p.330
	ENGINEER	p.217
	WARREN	pp.175;211
43.	WARREN	pp.177-181
	PERCE	p.68 Endnotes 227-8
44.	WOOD I	pp.64-5
	WARREN	pp.175, 220, 228
45.	PERCE	p.64 Endnotes 152-5
46.	WARREN	pp.187-210
	WARREN	pp.205-8
47.	WARREN	p.239
48.	SMILES	p.496
49.	WARREN	pp.228, 230
50.	JEAF	Vol.I p.155
51.	WARREN	p.293
52.	ScM	1970/473/7
53.	WARREN	p.257
54.	WARREN	pp.261-2
55.	WARREN	p.293
56.	WARREN	p.256
57.	WARREN	pp.252-3
58.	WARREN	pp.264-5
59.	WARREN	pp.76-7
60.	Private Collection	
61.	VULCAN	p.16
62.	WARREN	pp.305-7
63.	Proc. ICE	Vol.19 p.181
64.	WARREN	p.7
65.	ScM	1970/473/5
66.	JEAF	Vol.I p.131
67.	WARREN	p310
68.	PRO	RAIL 359/2
69.	JEAF	Vol.I p.181
70.	JEAF	Vol.I p.178
71.	JEAF	Vol.I p.180
72.	ROLT	p.225
73.	JEAF	Vol.I pp.182-3
74.	JEAF	Vol.I p.176
75.	Private Collection	
76.	WARREN	pp.311-5
	Drawing	p.310
77.	WARREN	p.79
78.	WARREN	p.325
79.	WARREN	p.315
80.	CONDER	p.14-15
81.	HLRO, Session 4, 1845	
82.	PRO	RAIL 772/34
83.	JEAF	Vol.I pp.187-8
84.	WARREN	p.86
85.	PERCE	p.65 Endnote 182
86.	PATENT 8998	
	WARREN	pp.346 – 370
87.	JEAF	Vol.I p.253
88.	WARREN	p.95
89.	JEAF	Vol.I pp.260-1
90.	ROY. SOC.	p.xxxi
91.	Proc. ICE	24 April 1855
92.	PERCE	p.69 Endnote 237
	Ev. AIRS	
93.	JEAF	Vol.II pp.232-3

INDEX